C000240676

WADERS

WADERS

NICHOLAS HAMMOND
BRUCE PEARSON

HAMLYN

First published in 1994 by Hamlyn Limited,
an imprint of Reed Consumer Books Ltd
Michelin House, 81 Fulham Road, London SW3 6RB
and Auckland, Melbourne, Singapore and Toronto

Copyright © Reed International Books Limited 1994

Text copyright © Nicholas Hammond 1994
Illustrations copyright © Bruce Pearson 1994
Map copyright © Reed International Books Limited 1994

ISBN 0 600 57974 3

All rights reserved. Apart from any fair dealing for the purpose of private
study, research, criticism or review, as permitted under the Copyright
Designs and Patents Act, 1988, no part of this publication may be
reproduced, stored in a retrieval system, or transmitted in any form or by
any means, electronic, electrical, chemical, mechanical, optical,
photocopying, recording, or otherwise, without prior written permission.
All enquiries should be addressed to the Publishers.

A CIP catalogue record for this book is available from the British Library

Page design by Jessica Caws
Map by Louise Griffiths

Printed in Hong Kong

CONTENTS

INTRODUCTION   6

MOVEMENTS   11

MIGRATION   11
Timing   13
Navigation   14
Journeys   17
Height of journeys   22
Speed of flight   23
Putting on weight   24
Composition of flocks   24
COLD-WEATHER MOVEMENTS   26
SEDENTARY WADERS   28

FEEDING   29

DIET   30
FEEDING METHODS   34
Feeding by sight   34
Feeding by swimming   43
Feeding by touch   43
ADAPTATIONS FOR FEEDING   50
THE PROBLEMS OF FINDING
   FOOD   55
WHERE WADERS FEED   57
TIMES OF FEEDING   57
FEEDING TERRITORIES   59

FLOCKING AND ROOSTING   62

THE BENEFITS AND COSTS OF
   FORMING FLOCKS   62
TIDAL ROOSTS   66
FLOCKS OF PLOVERS AND
   LAPWINGS   70

PLUMAGE AND MOULT   73

MOULT SEQUENCE   73
POST-BREEDING MOULT   78
PRE-BREEDING MOULT   80
BROOD-PATCHES   82
COLOUR CHANGES   82

COMFORT BEHAVIOUR   83

BATHING   83
OILING   83
PREENING   84
SCRATCHING   86
SKIN CARE   87
WING STRETCHING   87
SLEEPING AND RESTING   87

BREEDING   90

TIMING   90
SEXUAL DIMORPHISM   91
SITE FIDELITY   91
TERRITORY   92
ADVERTISING TERRITORY   96
COURTSHIP DISPLAYS   99
COPULATION   109
PAIR-BONDS   110
NESTS   113
EGGS   114
INCUBATION   117
GROWTH OF YOUNG   118
DEFENCE OF NESTS AND
   YOUNG   120
REACHING MATURITY   125

GAZETTEER   130

BIBLIOGRAPHY   169

SCIENTIFIC NAMES   170

INDEX   171

INTRODUCTION

No single English word defines adequately a group of birds as diverse as those most usually described as 'waders' or 'shorebirds'. Neither word is wholly definitive: not all waders wade and, although many are found on the shore at some stage in their lives, some rarely, if ever, see a seashore. However, most of the members of the nine families of waders do wade and are found at some point in their lives on the shores of rivers, lakes or seas.

Under conventional taxonomic arrangements waders are classed as members of the order Charadriiformes, which also covers sheathbills, skuas, gulls, terns, skimmers and auks. However, under the new avian taxonomy proposed by Sibley and Monroe on the basis of a technique known as 'DNA-DNA' hybridization, waders are assigned to the order Ciconiiformes which includes storks, raptors, grebes, gannets, herons, penguins, divers and petrels. Although this new classification begins, as do previous systems, with ostriches and finishes with perching birds, Sibley and Monroe have made radical rearrangements to the intervening groupings. In this book, however, we are working to the Voous order followed by *The Handbook of Birds of Europe, the Middle East and North Africa: The Birds of the Western Palearctic*.

Waders all share several obvious characteristics in physiology and behaviour. They generally share the obvious features of long or longish necks, long bills and long legs, but these vary with different species' behaviour and the way in which they have adapted to their particular habitats. Examine waders closely and you will see they have slit-shaped nostrils in the upper mandible. Usually each wing has eleven primaries, of which the eleventh, the farthest from the body, is very short and there are usually ten tail feathers. In most species there are two moults each year. Few species of waders need to perch and they do not, therefore, require a long hind toe. In most species it is rudimentary and in some, such as the ringed plovers, non-existent.

The young of waders are precocial, hatching with a covering of down, which is patterned to provide camouflage, and most are capable of feeding themselves. They leave the nest within days of hatching and remain with one or both parents at least until fledging.

The behavioural similarities are that most species are linked to water at some point in the year, that many migrate for long distances (a feature greatly welcomed by birdwatchers because it leads to waders turning up unexpectedly way beyond their normal ranges), and that outside the breeding season they are frequently gregarious.

The zoogeographical region covered in this book is known as the Western Palearctic, which extends south from Spitsbergen and Franz Josef Land to Mauritania and the southern border of Egypt, and east from the Azores to the Urals and the Caspian Sea (*see* maps on pages 127 and 128–9). There are eight families of waders within this region.

The painted-snipes, **Rostratulidae**, are medium-sized, long-billed, marsh-living waders. There are two species, one resident in Egypt.

Of the eleven species of oystercatchers, **Haematopodidae**, world-wide, only one breeds in the region. That is the Oystercatcher, a heavily built pied wader with a long, stout red bill.

Perhaps the most elegant family of waders is the stilts and avocets, **Recurvirostridae**, two species of which breed in the Western Palearctic. Both are long-legged and the Avocet has a bill that curves upwards.

The Crab Plover is the only member of the family **Dromadidae**, with its heavy, gull-like bill, it looks unlike any other wader. It breeds in Iraq on the margins of the region.

The thick-knees, **Burhinidae**, are medium-to-large waders with large eyes, thick bills and long legs with characteristically thick knee-joints. Of the world's nine species, two breed in the region. The Stone Curlew is a bird of dry, stony places and open plains, while the Senegal Thick-knee, which breeds in the Nile Valley, is rarely seen far from water.

The sixth family, **Glareolidae**, consists of pratincoles and coursers. Of the eight species, six have been recorded in the region. Of small to medium size, they are expert runners and all are pale in colour.

Plovers and lapwings form the **Charadriidae**, a family with a global membership of over 60 species, of which 19 have been recorded in the Western Palearctic. The stocky plovers vary from small to medium-sized with short necks and rounded foreheads, while the larger lapwings have longer necks, higher foreheads and, generally, a less round-shouldered posture than the plovers. Plumages tend to be boldly marked, often with black-and-white patterns.

The sandpipers and their allies form a family called **Scolopacidae**. There are 88 species, of which 57 have been recorded in the Western Palearctic and 43 breed or winter regularly here. They include the medium-sized, robust and long-billed woodcocks, of which one species is found here; five species of snipes, small to medium sized waders with long legs, very long bills and skulking habits; the small to medium-sized, highly migratory sandpipers, of which 21 species have been recorded in the Western Palearctic (11 are vagrants from North America

OVERLEAF *(top to bottom, left to right) Waders generally have long bills, necks and legs, with variations depending on habitat and behaviour (p. 8): Little Stint, Lapwing, Red-necked Phalarope, Cream-coloured Courser, Painted Snipe, Ringed Plover (p.9) Black-winged Stilt, Redshank, Oystercatcher, Stone Curlew, Woodcock and Crab Plover.*

or Eastern Asia); 20 species of godwits, curlews and 'shanks with long legs and long bills (five of these are American vagrants); and three species of small, fine-necked phalaropes, which are expert swimmers.

Waders show a wide and fascinating range of physiological and behavioural adaptations to the various habitats they use. These also enable different species to exploit different parts of the same habitat.

It seems that the waders' choices of habitats make them particularly vulnerable to human exploitation of their environment. The species that appear in huge numbers in autumn and winter on the intertidal sand-flats, mud-flats and estuaries of Western Europe breed on moorlands, tundra, wet-meadows, coasts, marshes and sometimes farmland. Despite their irreplaceable value as staging posts for waders and wildfowl, no estuary or tidal flat in Western Europe is safe from the opportunism of governments and developers. Although the immense financial costs have scotched massive reclamation proposals for the Wash, the Waddenzee and the Rhine delta in the past, today's threats come from smaller schemes and piecemeal developments which, in pursuit of human advantage of dubious value, constantly erode our estuaries.

Waders' breeding grounds also face threats. Trees are planted on moorland and wet-meadows, and fresh-water marshes, in which several species breed, are drained to create arable land, which is unsuitable breeding habitat for most species of waders. Britain will finish this century with less than one-tenth of the old meadowland with which it began it. Farming has intensified and fertilizers, pesticides and herbicides now mean it is unnecessary to let land lie fallow. Even for those waders, such as Lapwings and Stone Curlews, that will nest on arable land, the choice of nest-site is restricted, because winter-sown cereals are too well-grown by spring to provide breeding habitat for them.

The species that breed on the dwindling steppe-grasslands that once stretched from the Iberian Peninsula to Russia are also threatened with habitat loss. Typical bird communities of the steppes include Stone Curlews and Collared Pratincoles. Only a few remnants of natural steppe-grassland persist, the rest having been 'improved' to create deserts of wheat and barley. The continuing conversion of this grassland to arable farmland has severely reduced the numbers of breeding Caspian Plovers and Black-winged Pratincoles.

In the south of the region, the marshland breeding grounds of waders are threatened by both drainage and pollution. In Greece, for example, the wonderful wetlands of the Evros delta, the Nestos delta, Lake Mikitrou and Porto Lagos are all being damaged by drainage and pollution and the birds suffer from uncontrolled hunting.

Only by understanding and appreciating the complex lives of waders can we appreciate what needs to be done to conserve them. In the succeeding pages I shall attempt to describe and explain their behaviour.

MOVEMENTS

The need to find food is the reason for most bird movements. Migration, cold-weather movements, dispersive movements and the departure of one parent before the other and the young are all survival mechanisms. Almost all species of waders within the Western Palearctic have seasonal movements. It is on the southernmost edge of the region, where there is a consistent supply of food throughout the year, that they tend to be resident: the Painted Snipes and Kittlitz's Plovers of the Nile Delta rarely move from their breeding areas. In other species, the movements of different populations may vary: some are migratory, others dispersive and some resident. For example, the Spur-winged Plovers that breed in Turkey arrive from mid-March to mid-April and leave in August and September, probably for the Middle East. Those that breed in Israel are resident in their territories, but outside the breeding season they may form day-time flocks to find and exploit abundant sources of food, returning to their territories at night. Most winter flocks in Israel, however, are composed of young birds, unpaired birds together with winter visitors from Turkey and Greece. These flocks will wander extensively in search of food.

MIGRATION

Some waders travel thousands of kilometres in a year. The greatest travellers are the small sandpipers of the genus *Calidris*. The Sanderling breeds within the Arctic Circle and winters around coasts from Denmark to South Africa. Thus a Sanderling breeding in Siberia may reach the Cape of Good Hope by way of shores of the Baltic, the North Sea, the Atlantic and the Gulf of Guinea: a journey of some 17,000 kilometres. By the time it returns to its breeding grounds, the Sanderling may have travelled almost 40,000 km. One Sanderling ringed in winter in South Africa was recovered on the delta of the River Yenisey in Siberia in June. They are seen on coasts from northern Europe to Africa throughout the autumn, winter and spring and some ringed birds have been recovered on the coasts of the Caspian and Black seas.

Migration is hazardous and the longer the journey the greater the hazards. Nevertheless, despite the high costs, it is a system that has great benefits. Migrants are able to exploit the food supplies

Long-distance migrants, Sanderlings migrate from their breeding grounds in Siberia along the coasts of Europe and Africa to South Africa.

available for limited periods in some areas, so they can rear more young than they would be able to if they remained in one area throughout the year.

The climates and habitats of the world are not constant. During successive glaciations in the Northern Hemisphere, birds were prevented from living in vast areas, but as the ice retreated vegetation appeared, followed by animals, including birds, which were quick to exploit the newly released food sources. The retreat of the ice was gradual and sporadic: each winter ice and snow covered again ground which had been exposed during the preceding summer, but birds were able to move south to areas where there was food.

Today, in the boggy tundra of the Arctic Circle, the process continues. During summer there are abundant supplies of flying insects and almost 24 hours of daylight gives breeding birds excellent feeding opportunities. Consequently they breed more successfully than would be possible in their wintering grounds, where competition for food and nesting space would be greater. However, the brevity of the northern summer means that the birds have developed breeding strategies to ensure they rear as many young as possible in the time available.

Although the reason for migration from the breeding grounds in late summer and early autumn is the need for food and back in spring the need to breed, the stimulus to migrate in autumn is not actual food shortage. If a bird were to wait until food supplies ran low, it would be unable to undertake the migration, because it needs to feed to have the energy to migrate. Stimulus, then, comes from external factors such as changes in daylight, temperature or barometric pressure, or from physiological changes within the bird, a form of internal clock.

In spring, the sexual cycle is stimulated by changes in daylight and temperature and, for birds already on migration, sudden falls in temperature may cause a reverse migration. However, the birds cannot afford to miscalculate their return to their breeding grounds. If they arrive too soon, they may find feeding difficult, but if they are late, they will not be able to make the most of the very short breeding season and may breed unsuccessfully.

Timing

Just as the timing of migration appears to be genetically programmed, so does the impulse to migrate. Experimental selective breeding of migrating Blackcaps, a species with resident and migratory populations, showed that the migratory trait in the offspring increased with selective breeding, as did the sedentary trait among the resident Blackcaps.

It is beneficial for a species to have some populations which migrate and others that are resident because each may be in a position to take advantage of variations in weather. Thus, in an unusually early spring, residents can breed early, but in a hard winter and cold spring, during which populations of residents may be devastated, the summer migrants will have survived.

Changes in migratory behaviour can take place very quickly. An increasing number of Blackcaps have wintered in Britain in the last 25 years. Among waders some Little Ringed Plovers, summer migrants, which were first recorded as British breeding birds in the middle of this century, now overwinter here.

These adjustments in behaviour can happen very rapidly: within five to ten generations populations of partially migrant birds can change from resident to migrant.

Movements of waders are not confined to spring and autumn migrations. There are wader movements throughout the year. Species do not all breed at the same time and within species, different populations behave differently. As Sanderlings reach their tundra breeding grounds in late May and early June Lapwings in England, with their young having fledged, move in family groups away from their breeding territories. Farther south, the breeding season for Cream-coloured Coursers on the Canary Isles begins in February and most young have fledged by the end of April.

Species which share the same breeding grounds do not all move simultaneously. Of those that breed in Scandinavia, family parties of Lapwings, Ruffs and Curlews begin to move south in May, with peak numbers in June and July. Then towards the end of May, the southward movement of Redshanks, Spotted Redshanks and Oystercatchers begins. Bar-tailed Godwits begin to leave in July, with peak numbers towards the end of the month and in early August. Last to leave are juvenile Dunlins which remain until early September, most of the adults having left in mid-August.

Early in the migration season, birds can afford to wait for optimal weather conditions of a following wind and good visibility. However, as the period of migration proceeds there is an increasing risk of reaching the breeding grounds too late for successful breeding. In autumn, late departure may mean that the bird reaches the staging posts on the way south at a time when the food stocks have been depleted. The later birds, therefore, faced with such urgency, have less choice of weather conditions in which to migrate.

Migrants also seem to choose particular times of day. To make the six-hour crossing from the North Sea shores of Germany and the Netherlands to eastern Britain, Lapwings leave about three hours before sunset, completing their journey in the dark. However, most of the waders arriving on the east coast in autumn do so in the early morning.

Navigation

Post-war developments in radar studies of bird migration have helped to reveal the routes migrants take and to raise questions about how birds navigate. It seems that birds' built-in time-keeping programme, called circadian rhythm, can be used in conjunction with sun and stars to navigate. That continental Lapwings begin to cross the North Sea in daylight and arrive, having held the same course, after dusk, suggests that they must use both the sun and the stars. But the fact that they can compensate for wind and correct to the same course even on overcast nights suggests that there are other elements to their navigation.

As the young of some species of birds appear to able to make long migratory journeys on their own, along routes that they have never travelled before, it seems that they must have an inherited ability to navigate using the Earth's magnetic field. In other words, they have a

*When they cross the North Sea, Lapwings leave three hours before
sunset and arrive in Britain after dark.*

form of inbuilt magnetic compass, but where this is situated or how it
functions is still unclear. Research suggests that use of the magnetic
compass is most important in young, inexperienced birds.

The sun is easy to see on a clear day, but even when there is
partial cloud cover birds seem to be able to identify the position of
the sun. Evidence suggests that experienced birds orientate with
compass bearings on a few landmarks. This avoids the need to clutter
their brains with a mass of remembered detail. A journey over land
becomes 'south from the reedmarsh, then south-west at the long,
narrow lake and west at the pointed mountain' rather than a
remembered route that fills in the the detail between these landmarks.

As well as visual landmarks there may be olfactory and aural
landmarks. Migrant waders may be attuned to the variations in the
smells of seawater, fresh water and degrees of brackishness or the
seaweed cast up on western-facing beaches in autumn. The sensitivity
of birds' hearing means that they can probably pick up differences in
sounds that the human ear cannot appreciate, but which give clues to
the nature of the landscape, an ability that would be particularly
valuable on a dark night.

Journeys

There are two major flyways of waders through the Western Palearctic region. The largest of these takes Arctic breeding birds south-westwards along the western coasts of Europe and down the coast of west Africa. The waders that use this eastern Atlantic flyway are joined in Ireland and Britain by waders from northern Canada and Greenland, which have passed south-eastwards through Iceland. Each autumn and winter over three million waders use the flyway, over a third of them stopping at British and Irish estuaries.

The other major route is from Russia south-south-westwards to Turkey across the Mediterranean and southwards via the Gulf of Suez or down through Israel's Arava Valley and directly down the Gulf of Aqaba. The eastern migrants include Broad-billed and Marsh Sandpipers, Black-tailed Godwits and Caspian Plovers. Large numbers of waders use this route but not in the large flocks seen along the eastern Atlantic flyway nor is the migration as impressive as the flocks of soaring migrant storks and raptors which pass down the eastern side of the Western Palearctic.

Different populations of the same species may take different routes. Many Ringed Plovers from Siberia take the eastern route, but some move across Europe and mingle on British estuaries with birds of the same species from Canada and Greenland. Similarly, most of the Redshanks wintering in Britain and Ireland are Icelandic or home-bred birds that have dispersed from their breeding grounds. Of the slightly smaller Scandinavian Redshanks, Danish breeding birds winter mainly in the western Mediterranean which they seem to reach by flying on a broad front overland, while Swedish and Norwegian birds move around the coast of western Europe to winter in west Africa.

The Icelandic race of the Black-tailed Godwit, which has a shorter bill than the European race, winters mainly in Ireland and southern England, but as the population has increased some have begun to winter in Iberia. The European race moves farther south, mostly wintering in Africa north of the Equator. Many of the birds move along the coast of western Europe, but the comparative paucity of godwits in southern Morocco and at the Mauritanian Banc d'Arquin suggests that they may cross the desert in a non-stop migration rather than moving around the coast to reach their sub-Saharan wintering

The two main flyways for waders through the Western Palearctic region. On the western route birds from northern Canada and Greenland join birds from northern Scandinavia and Siberia in Britain and Ireland, moving south through Spain and north-west Africa. On the other route birds from northern Russia pass through the Black Sea, Turkey, Israel and the Nile Valley.

Recent sightings of the extremely rare Slender-billed Curlew have only been on migration. Here three are resting with a flock of Black-tailed Godwits in Morocco.

grounds. There is also a passage of Black-tailed Godwits through the Black Sea and Israel, but this involves fewer birds than the western movement.

Sightings of some species on migration may be the only clue to their status. The very rare Slender-billed Curlew breeds in south-west Siberia and migrates to north-west Africa, passing to the north of the Caspian Sea, along the northern coast of the Black Sea and across Greece and Italy. Its breeding grounds are remote and, despite recent expeditions, no nests have been found during the second half of this century. However, it is still seen on migration, but these records are sporadic: about 150 sightings in 20 years. Each year these are becoming rarer and fewer than ten individuals were seen in 1991. BirdLife International estimates that there are probably between 50 and 200 individuals left in the world.

In autumn and winter, some discrete breeding populations of the same species mingle. For example, the Ringed Plovers found around British and Irish shores are a mixture of western breeders from Iceland

and Greenland, breeders from Scandinavia and Russia and British and Irish residents. In other species, the breeding populations remain separate. The Oystercatchers wintering on the west coast of Britain and Ireland are largely of Scottish and Irish origin while those on the east coast of Britain are predominantly from Scandinavia and Russia with some local birds, and others from Faeroe and the Netherlands.

While many Scandinavian and Russian Oystercatchers stick to the east coast, the Bar-tailed Godwits and Grey Plovers from Siberia arrive on the east coast and later some move to the west. In July and August, some Oystercatchers arriving in the Firth of Forth and at Teesmouth on the Northumberland coast will fly overland to estuaries on the west coast of Scotland. In August, Whimbrels, Curlews, Ringed Plovers and Dunlins cross the country. The Dunlins at Teesmouth in August and early September are Icelandic. These are followed by juvenile birds that have hatched in Siberia and, in October, by adults from Siberia.

It seem that among waders larger birds may not travel so far on migration. Whimbrels, for example, tend to breed farther north and to winter farther south than the larger curlews. Even within a species there may be differences in the migratory behaviour between large and small birds. Among Ringed Plovers the largest birds tend to be those that do not travel as far north to breed or as far south to winter. The

Ringed Plovers from Greenland and Northern Europe stay for no more than three weeks on the coasts of Western Europe before moving south. Many locally breeding birds stay all winter.

larger birds, therefore, travel less far. The relative proximity of their wintering and breeding grounds in the temperate zones means the larger birds move to their breeding grounds as soon as spring begins, but such a theory ignores the costs to the smaller birds which have to migrate further. Avoidance of competition for winter feeding could be another reason for the smaller birds moving south in winter. The later onset of the breeding season in the Arctic means that the northerly breeders can use the same feeding grounds as the temperate breeders once they have moved to their breeding areas. The smaller birds feed and then overfly the larger birds to reach their more northerly breeding grounds in time for the start of the shorter summer.

Not all migrant waders are dependent on estuaries and coasts as staging posts. Dotterels breed on open, flat and sparsely vegetated uplands and winter on the stony steppe, ploughed farmland and semi-desert of north Africa and the Middle East. They cross Europe on a broad front, stopping at a few traditional stopping points where they are seen in small parties of up to 20 birds. Records of 'hundreds' of birds are rare. In the Netherlands, Dotterels prefer to pause on the lower-lying, western areas and in the steppes of Hungary and the Ukraine, they choose those where the soils are lighter. They pass through England on their way north to Scotland in late April and early May, pausing at traditional sites such as low chalkland slopes in Cambridgeshire, the low hills behind the north Norfolk coast and Pendle Hill in Lancashire. It appears that they are also faithful to traditional wintering areas.

The strong attachment of Green Sandpipers to fresh water is maintained both in their choice of breeding habitat and on migration. They breed in a band across the sub-Arctic woodlands across Eurasia from Norway. They migrate on a broad front overland and singly or in small groups and winter sparsely across Europe, north Africa, sub-Saharan Africa, India and south-east Asia. Southward passage

Juvenile Dunlins (top) from Siberia arrive on the Northumberland coast in September, to be followed by adults in October.

begins in Finland with females leaving in the first half of June. The first birds cross western Europe in the second half of the month. Although some are south of the Sahara by early August, most arrive there in September.

Another inland-nesting wader that does not use estuaries or coasts is the Stone Curlew. There is a distinct south-westward movement in autumn. Small flocks are formed in late summer before they move south. In milder winters, some that breed in England will winter in the south of the country, but most move to Iberia or north Africa. Waders of the steppes tend to move on a broad front across Europe to Africa. Black-winged Pratincoles from the Ukraine, Russia and Kazakhstan cross Turkey, Iran and Iraq to Africa south of the equator. The more common Collared Pratincoles move south on broad fronts in larger flocks to winter to the south of the Sahara Desert.

For many of the waders that fly south from the Arctic every autumn, the estuaries around the coasts of western Europe are staging posts at which to feed and rest before before moving on. For example, western populations of Ringed Plovers from Iceland and Greenland, and those from Scandinavia and Russia, stay for no more than three weeks before moving south. Many of the 3,000,000 wintering waders around the British and Irish coasts move between estuaries.

Although some waders winter on the bays along the western coast of France, large numbers continue south. About 100,000 winter along the Atlantic coast of Morocco, but between 600,000 and 900,000 waders pass through on spring migration, pausing on the marshes and lagoons which stretch south along the coast from the estuary of the Marbor to Puerto Cansado. Approximately three million waders winter south of the Sahara, along the coasts of the Gulf of Guinea and the inland wetlands of west Africa.

Height of journeys

Wind is an important factor with which migrating birds have to contend, especially those that are travelling towards the west. The prevailing winds in western Europe are westerly which means that, for a large part of their journeys, migrating waders in autumn have to face head winds.

Studies have shown that migrants will wait for favourable winds. When there is a following north-easterly wind in autumn the greatest number of birds migrate, the density is reduced when there is a head wind. When a flock of waders is airborne the birds seek the altitude at which the wind-speed is greatest. Wind-speed varies with altitude, particularly when the weather is changeable. Flying in the face of a cyclone, which creates a whirling mixture of wind-speeds and directions, the migrating birds will seek the most suitable.

Flying at normal or higher temperatures burns more fat and creates heat, using water within the body. So, a bird loses more water than it would normally through metabolism. This dehydration can be reduced by flying when temperatures are lower. This includes night-time and flying at high enough altitudes to reach cool air, which effectively cools the bird in the same way that early biplanes relied on air-cooled engines. Flying at a higher altitude, though, may lower the oxygen intake, but as well as reducing dehydration, there is the added advantage of increased speed because air density is lower and wind-speeds greater.

Lapwings seem to migrate across the North Sea at a mean of over 1000 m with a following wind, but they will fly much lower, just above the waves, when there is a head wind or rain. This is because wind-speed is lowest close the surface. On land this practice makes the birds follow physical features, such as mountains, ridges and shore-lines. Birds will sometimes even deviate from their original or normal routes. Radar tracking of Lapwings suggests that they will rise to whatever altitude is most beneficial and keep to it.

Colonel Meinertzhagen listed altitudes for all kinds of birds in 1955 based on observations from aeroplanes. From these it is clear that waders can achieve great heights if necessary and mountain ranges seem to present no problems. Curlews and godwits were recorded at 6000 metres flying south in autumn across the Himalayas and sandpipers, flying east in spring, passed over France in an easterly direction at 3658 m. It is probable that these high-flying birds have climbed higher as they lost weight as 'fuel' was used and consequently were able to take advantage of the greater speed at the higher levels.

Speed of flight

Birds may fly faster on migration than in normal flight and it seems that spring migration is undertaken more quickly than autumn migration. While the northward-bound migrants are stimulated by the onset of breeding, they are also often helped in their north-easterly movement by prevailing westerly and south-westerly winds. Waders put on more weight before spring migration than before autumn migration. The added weight enables them to fly for longer without stopping to refuel.

Lapwings crossing the North Sea in autumn moved at 55–75 kph while flocks of passerines moved at about 38 kph: the differences in speeds help observers differentiate between flocks of Lapwings and thrushes which produce very similar patterns on a radar screen. Golden Plovers fly faster and Meinertzhagen gives their speed on migration as 96 kph.

Putting on weight

The energy needed for migration comes from reserves of fat built up during the waders' pauses at their estuarine and mud-flat staging posts. Common Sandpipers that have wintered in South Africa double their mean winter weight before beginning their return journey in March. Pausing on the northward journey the sandpipers are able to replenish their energy reserves.

The maximum weight of a breeding Dunlin is 53 g, but in the weeks prior to northward migration those on the Cheshire Dee increase by 0.57 g per day during the first half of May. With a weight of 75–80g when they take off, their energy reserves are more than adequate for the journey, but on reaching the Arctic they may need their remaining reserves.

The birds have no way of forecasting the weather on their breeding grounds. The ice-free period is short and, if they arrive too early, they may have to rely on their stores of fat until the ice melts and they can feed again, or until their invertebrate food emerges.

Many waders use staging posts short of their destination in order to build up energy reserves in case conditions at their breeding grounds are inhospitable. Thus, Knots which should be capable of flying direct from the British Isles to Greenland nevertheless use Iceland as a staging post. Sanderlings add almost two-thirds of their lean weight before migration, providing them with sufficient energy for a 5000-km flight. In spring, the fat is deposited very quickly, at slightly less than 4 g per day, during their 10-week stay on the Wash and it provides enough energy to fly direct to their Greenland breeding grounds, apparently overflying Iceland. On the return autumn journey Sanderlings have been reported arriving in Morocco apparently exhausted after a long flight.

Before migration, Bar-tailed Godwits accumulate fat reserves, some of which are still there on arrival, but their muscle weight is lower. This suggests that the muscles are used as a protein reserve and that the remaining fat is a reserve to be used in breeding or in the event of inadequate food on arrival.

Composition of flocks

Migrating flocks of waders may be composed predominantly of members of one sex or age category. Flocks of Curlews or Dunlins may be mainly adult or juvenile. In the north of their range within the Arctic Circle, female Dunlins begin to move south before either the males or the young. Similarly, male Redshanks stay with the young while the female migrates. In Scandinavia, female Spotted Redshanks leave their families in June. There is a possible survival value for the

Golden Plovers fly fast on migration and may fly faster than Lapwings which have been been recorded crossing the North Sea at up to 75 kph.

species if females migrate earlier: they can go to better feeding areas and reduce competition for food on the breeding grounds.

Some species, such as Redshanks in Britain, move in family flocks to coasts where they join with larger flocks or, as is the case with Golden Plovers and Lapwings, until they meet other family parties. The plovers stay together as families, but in many species the adults leave the breeding grounds to migrate south before their offspring. The first-year birds, which having recently fledged do not need to moult, can continue to feed while stocks last before moving south.

The Dunlin is an example of a species in which the adults of some populations move south before their offspring. This gives them an opportunity to find the best roosting sites and those that arrive in late August and early September on the Waddenzee occupy the best sites on low islands and islets. The juveniles which arrive in late September and early October have to settle on the less desirable roosts nearer the shore.

A curious piece of Dunlin behaviour is associated with its role as 'the plover's page', a Scottish name for this species. It has been suggested that this is because it arrives at its breeding grounds a few days in advance of the Golden Plover. However, C. Oakes argued in *British Birds*, a more likely explanation is the habit of Dunlins associating with the plovers with single Dunlins standing behind the flock in the position of a page and of keeping this station even when the flock is disturbed and moves to another field. He also pointed out that the Dunlin's Icelandic name 'louthrall' means 'plover's slave'. Association of Dunlins with Golden Plovers gives them certain feeding advantages. The larger, more nervous Golden Plovers act as sentries for the Dunlins, which are able to feed much less warily than if they were on their own. Perhaps the plovers should be called the Dunlin's slaves.

Most migrant waders travel in flocks, but some wait until they reach their winter quarters before forming large flocks. Dotterels that breed in Scotland and Scandinavia travel south on broad fronts across Europe in small parties, rarely of more than fifteen birds. They form larger flocks of several hundreds of birds on arrival in their North African winter quarters.

Among the least sociable of waders are Common Sandpipers, which migrate singly or in very small flocks: more than 20 birds together would be exceptional. When they stop to feed they keep considerable individual distances between each other and from other waders. The Sociable Plover, by contrast, lives up to its name, both during the breeding season and outside it, but the flocks it forms are not large. Post-breeding flocks of up to 1000 have been recorded in Kazakhstan and flocks of several hundreds have been recorded in winter quarters in Iraq, Iran and Pakistan, but groups of fifteen to 20 birds are more usual.

COLD-WEATHER MOVEMENTS

Although weather conditions may directly facilitate, in the case of cyclones, or retard, in the case of head winds, bird movements, the effect of weather is largely indirect. Hard weather conditions may prevent the birds from feeding so that, to find food, they have to move. In the vast complex of estuaries and flats to be found around the coasts of Britain and Ireland and the North Sea coasts of

The Dunlin's habit of consorting with flocks of Golden Plovers has given it the name 'plover's page'. The plovers are more nervous and by associating with them the Dunlins are able to feed less warily, because the plovers will give the alarm when danger approaches.

mainland Europe, there is a wintering population of waders and wildfowl which moves between the open, unfrozen feeding areas.

When these feeding grounds freeze they usually do so first on the European mainland, which precipitates a south-westward movement of all the waders wintering in north-west Europe. For example, the Lapwings which cross the North Sea from Scandinavia, Germany and the Netherlands to escape freezing continental weather displace the population already wintering in England and Scotland. The displaced birds move west and which in turn displace Welsh and Irish winterers which move south to Spain. When the weather improves, the displaced birds all move back. In the exceptional hard winter of 1962–63, Lapwings moved as far south as Morocco. Their arrival coincided with an unusually wet period caused by the southerly track of a depression and providing excellent feeding for the displaced Lapwings. In other hard winters, Lapwings may reach the Canaries and Madiera.

SEDENTARY WADERS

In Egypt, Painted Snipes are sedentary, apparently not moving away from their breeding areas in the Nile Delta and the Faiyum. In other parts of their range they may make short migrations. Their rounded wings are comparatively short compared with those of long-distance migrants.

Another Egyptian breeding wader is Kittlitz's Plover, which is found breeding on the banks of rivers and open grassy plains. The Egyptian population is sedentary, but elsewhere in Africa Kittlitz's Plovers make local seasonal movements.

FEEDING

Food provides the energy that enables a bird to sustain its way of life. The level of energy expenditure of a bird when it is not active, unfed and in an environment where a body temperature of 20 °C can be maintained by the insulation of feathers rather than increased metabolic activity is described as its basal metabolic rate. It is measured by the consumption of oxygen or the production of carbon dioxide as the bird breathes. If the air temperature drops, a stationary bird has to expend energy in generating heat by metabolism and the moment it moves more energy is expended. Day-to-day energy expenditure may be up to ten times greater than the basal metabolic rate.

A number of factors alter energy requirements. Variations may result from the time of day, season or outside temperature. Basal metabolic rates increase during the hours when the bird is normally active, whether it is active or not. The rates among migrants decrease when they are in the tropics and increase when they are in a colder climate.

Thus, the amount of food a bird takes each day will differ between individuals and will need to be higher when the temperature is lower. It is difficult to calculate how much food a wild bird eats each day. To do so ornithologists must measure the time spent feeding, must identify the species of prey taken, must measure the rate of intake, must estimate the size of prey taken and must measure the energetic content of each type of prey. Various studies into how much of the food taken by waders is ingested suggests that between 80 per cent and 90 per cent is assimilated. The remainder is excreted as droppings or regurgitated as pellets of indigestible material. The identifiable fragments of shells in waders' pellets help to give an indication of the species on which they are feeding.

For birds, finding food is not consistently easy. In extremely cold weather or drought, food may be difficult to find and in cold weather there is an additional problem of needing extra energy to maintain body temperature. Storage of energy is a mechanism through which this potential lack of food can be overcome. Eating food can supply sufficient energy for the bird to survive several subsequent days without feeding. Thus, in the maritime climate of the eastern Atlantic and North Sea coasts waders reach their peak weight in mid-winter when frozen conditions may make feeding impossible. Only exceptionally does this strategy fail dramatically when the frozen conditions last for many days.

In the days following an enforced fasting during a hard spell, a wader eats more than usual in order to reach basal metabolic rate and to compensate for the energy lost by its vigorous feeding.

In spring, extra energy is needed by females for egg production and by males for display and territorial defence and, as we have seen, the Arctic breeders of both sexes need to build up fat reserves in case there is a shortage of food on their breeding grounds. If there is no such shortage, the fat reserves are used. This allows the birds to spend less time feeding and more on other activities. During the breeding season, fat reserves are generally unnecessary because food is plentiful unless there are periods of exceptionally hard weather. To build up fat would make the bird heavier and therefore require extra energy expenditure which be better used in egg production and feeding young.

In autumn, waders must eat more to maintain body weight and to build fat reserves and muscle again for migration. However, during the energy-expensive activity of moult (*see* page 73) waders need to keep their weight low to compensate for less aerodynamic efficiency because the wing area is reduced as feathers are lost. The heavier a bird is the less rapidly it can accelerate and the less manoeuvrable it is in the air. Therefore, it is more likely to be caught by a predator and, because it has high reserves of fat, it is a better catch.

The daily energy budget varies between species. Small waders require proportionally more food than larger species. Similarly, energy requirements will vary with the feeding behaviour of different species. The stealthy feeders, which stand and wait for their prey, use less energy than the chasers and consequently may need less food.

Where the wader winters also has an effect on fat reserves. Those that winter in the tropics and sub-tropics have a less abundant but more constant food supply and have no need of fat reserves to take them through the frosty days.

DIET

Waders feed mainly on invertebrates, but some also eat seeds and berries. Naturally, the prey taken varies between species and, within species, between seasons, habitats and individuals. The amounts of types of each prey taken also vary because the density of prey changes, as do the needs of the waders. Before migration and during cold weather fat reserves must be built up. When females are laying, the calcium needed is often obtained from eggshells and rodent bones.

The estuaries and coasts where waders feed in winter are probably the most productive of all the habitats in the region and are among the most productive ecosystems in the world. Along the long coastlines of north-western Europe, it is the sheltered estuaries that are particularly valuable as feeding grounds for waders. The rivers bring fresh water, which is high in nutrients, to mix in the estuaries with salt water. The resulting submerged mud-flats, intertidal mud-flats and sand-flats, raised and submerged salt-marshes support an abundance of invertebrates of a limited range of species.

The invertebrates on which waders feed include polychaete worms, molluscs and crustaceans whose food includes detritus, bacteria, microscopic animals, marine plants and, in some cases, each other. They are breathtakingly abundant, but their density varies and there is a direct relationship between abundance of food and numbers of waders. Because many of these invertebrates can burrow, they are able to survive in very cold weather by disappearing into the mud. In colder weather they become less active and burrow deeper. They become less easy for waders to find as their inactivity decreases the number of clues to their whereabouts and they may burrow beyond the reach of some waders. Other invertebrates, such as shrimps and crabs, may move into deeper water which may put them beyond the reach of waders.

The range of invertebrates taken by waders is extensive, but short descriptions are given below of the species that are particularly important as food for waders. Polychaete worms feed on bacteria, organic detritus, algae and protozoa found in the sand or mud. To ingest their food they also have to take in large amounts of mud or sand. Among the material taken in, only about 0.05 per cent by weight is edible. This means that a Lugworm (*arenicola*) must consume up to 10 g of mud or sand each day in order to survive. Within two years every grain of sand within the immediate vicinity of the burrow to a depth of 10 cm will have passed through the Lugworm.

Although Lugworms spend their lives beneath the mud, their whereabouts is easy to see because each lives in a 'U'-shaped burrow. One end shows as a shallow depression on the surface, which is caused by the sand collapsing as the Lugworm ingests it, and the other is marked by a twisting cast of defecated material. At intervals of about 45 minutes the Lugworm moves backwards up the shaft to defecate, when it becomes particularly vulnerable to the bill of a probing wader. Burrowing to a depth of 10 cm the Lugworm is beyond the reach of many waders when it is at the deepest part of the burrow.

The Rag Worm (*Nereis diversicolor*), another burrowing polychaete worm, is an important source of food for waders. Its vertical burrow has several other shafts running obliquely to the surface and may continue on the surface as a tunnel of mucous. Rag Worms are opportunist feeders. The front ends of their bodies protrude from the burrow as they grab small animals, green algae and other organic remnants.

Anyone who has lifted up stranded seaweed on a British beach will have seen sandhoppers (*gammarus*), which look like little brown shrimps and are important food for Turnstones and Purple Sandpipers.

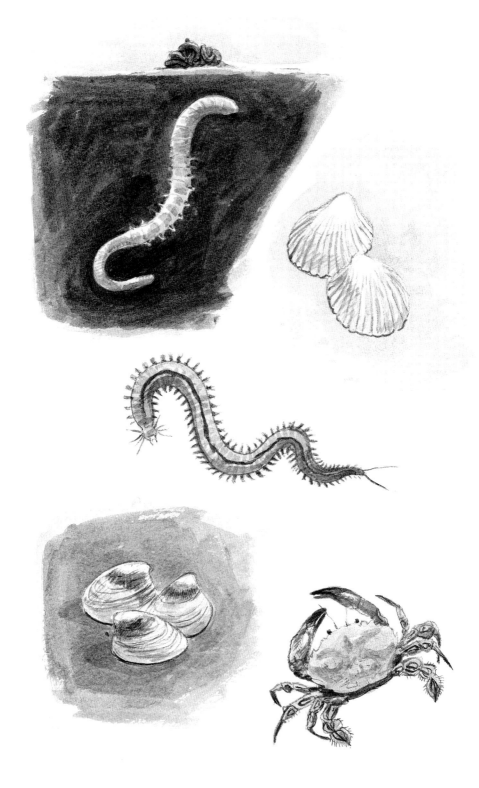

Another shrimp-like crustacean important for waders is *Corophium volutator*. Up to 1.5 cm long, it lives in a shallow 'U'-shaped burrow. Using its long antennae it pulls grains of sand and mud into its burrow. It can also feed by filtering animal life from the water. This shrimp readily comes to the surface when the temperature of the mud is above 4 °C. Heavy rain drives it underground.

Molluscs have adapted well to life on estuaries and coastal waters. Both cockles and mussels feature in the diet of waders. Oystercatchers have heavy enough bills to cope with both of these relatively large bivalves, taking cockles from beneath the sand and mussels from rocks. Another group of bivalves is the tellins, which look like small, smooth-shelled cockles. They burrow beneath the mud, using a long, manoeuvrable siphon to 'hoover' the surface for food. A single Knot may feed on 700 tellins in a day. The Baltic Tellin (*Macoma balthica*) is the dominant bivalve of the Baltic on the soft muddy beaches below sea-level, but in the Gulf of Bothnia, where the water contains only a tenth of the salts normally found in sea, the tellin is replaced by other relict animals. In Britain, *macoma* is predominant in slightly salted water.

Among the snail-like molluscs, the tiny Laver Spire Shell (*hydrobia*), which feeds in huge numbers on mud (up to 40,000 per square metre) and a green seaweed, *Enteromorpha intestinalis*, is important as a source of food for waders and wildfowl. Winkles of various species occupy different parts of the shore and are a source of wader food, especially for Purple Sandpiper.

The thick, spiralling shell of the Dog Whelk (*Nucella lapillus*) gives it protection from the attentions of waders, but Oystercatchers and Purple Sandpipers can both tackle the whelks when they are on move with a large part of their bodies out of their shells.

On rocky shores, the monovalve limpets have to be able to cling to rocks washed twice a day by incoming tides and twice a day by outgoing tides. The other hazard that they face is predation by waders. They are at their most vulnerable when they move and quick-sighted Oystercatchers and Turnstones may prise them from their rocks.

Parasites on molluscs may be transferred to birds when the molluscs are eaten. A parasitic worm in the Dog Whelk emasculates its host and causes it to change from being gregarious to being solitary and move into the open, where it is more vulnerable to predation by birds, which in turn become hosts to the parasites. Similar parasites are found in other molluscs. Oystercatchers have been seen to reject paraticized tellins, but younger birds appear either to be less experienced in detecting the parasites or are forced to eat affected tellins because of food shortages.

The mud-flats of the North Sea coasts and estuaries are rich in food for birds. Among their main foods are: Lugworms, Rag Worms, Corophium, cockles, tellins, Laver Spire Shells and small crabs.

Crabs are predatory crustaceans, which can move quickly and cover large areas, but they in turn fall prey to birds. Oystercatchers, Greenshanks and Curlews will feed extensively on crabs. Competition between species is avoided in the Waddenzee where Greenshanks take smaller crabs than Curlews.

Berries may be an important food for waders when invertebrates are scarce. They have been found in the guts of many species including Bar-tailed Godwits, Curlews and Golden Plovers at both the beginning and the end of the breeding season. Woodcocks have been seen feeding extensively on blackberries and, when snow or frost makes probing for worms impossible, they will feed on plant material, mainly seeds and tufts of cotton-grass.

Seeds and other plant materials are taken in varying quantities by waders. About 10 per cent of the food of Lapwings, for example, is plant material, largely seeds and grasses. But the stomachs of five birds examined in December, after a very hard frost and the ground covered by snow contained nothing but cow-dung. The Golden Plovers, which feed alongside Lapwings in winter, showed similar vegetable food, but examination of the stomach contents of Golden Plovers taken in June on moorland in Estonia showed that 12 per cent was plant material including cranberries and crowberries. The proportion increased in July and by August plant material was the predominant food. In the stomachs of 40 birds taken in autumn in the Hebrides almost a quarter of the material was moss, green leaves and some seeds.

FEEDING METHODS

Waders find their prey by sight or by touch, sometimes by a combination of both and sometimes by hearing. How they feed depends on their prey and where they feed.

Feeding by sight

Sight-feeding waders are characterized by short bills and acute eyesight. When they are feeding by sight, waders tend to be well-spaced. If they are too close to each other they waste time and energy when two birds see the same prey and both dash for it. The distraction of the other bird will make each one a less efficient hunter and the prey is more likely to escape. Interference when feeding,

On rocky shores and among the seaweed cast up by the waves there is plentiful food for waders: mussels, Dog Whelks, winkles, limpets, crabs and Gammarus shrimps.

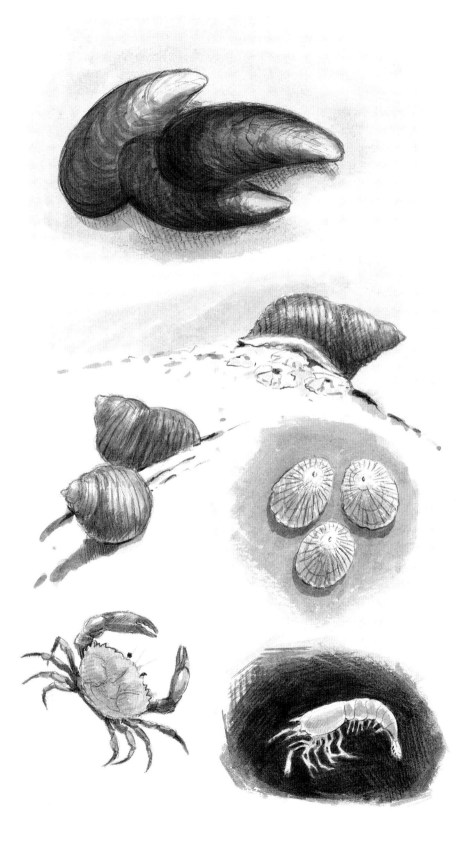

therefore, costs time and energy with no obvious advantage. It is better for every bird to be able to feed at a sufficient distance from the next to prevent interference.

Plovers and Lapwings are sight-feeders and all species use the same 'run-and-pause' technique. They dash forward, pause and bend their heads rapidly to catch sight or sound of their prey. This behaviour gives them the appearance of long-legged thrushes and when they pause and crouch they are locating earthworms, often by ear. Grey Plovers seem to have greater than 90 per cent success in finding food when pecking at the surface.

Plovers and Lapwings use 'foot-trembling', tapping rapidly on the ground to disturb its prey and to trick it into moving and disclosing its whereabouts. Foot-trembling may also bring invertebrates to the surface in the same way that the vibrations of traffic may bring them to the surface of motorway verges, behaviour which is exploited by Rooks and Black-headed Gulls. Dotterels have been seen to foot-tremble on short turf on Pendle Hill in Lancashire. Grey Plovers will flick at the surface of the mud to expose prey just beneath the surface. Golden Plovers often feed at night, taking worms in winter pasture, which suggests that they may also use hearing in discovering prey.

Strong winds on mud-flats make feeding by sight in exposed positions difficult, because the prey may burrow beneath the mud and wind rippling the surface of shallow water makes it difficult for the bird to see anything in the water. It seems that Grey Plovers' choice of feeding territories is influenced by the desirability of sheltered feeding.

The Dunlin has three feeding techniques: pecking at the surface of the mud, probing the mud (a touch-feeding technique) and 'stitching' with a sewing-machine action of probing very rapidly (another touch technique). The pecks at the surface are preceded by a dash forward which is typical of sight-feeders. Their feeding is dictated by the tides and they will feed during both day and night mostly on the intertidal flats, but also on salt-marsh.

The behaviour of Redshanks feeding on mud-flats changes with the time of day. During the hours of daylight they feed on the shrimp *Corophium volutato*) which they find by sight because parts of the shrimps' bodies stick up from the mud. Because sight-feeding is more

Grey Plovers feed with plenty of distance between them, locating their food with a thrush-like 'run-and-pause' technique, pecking at items on the surface of the mud.

On rocky and shingly shores Turnstones search for invertebrates beneath the flotsam on the tide line while Oystercatchers and Purple Sandpipers feed on mussels among the rocks.

efficient when individuals keep their distance, the flocks of day-feeding Redshanks are much looser than at night, when they switch to snails (*Hydrobia ulvae*), which they find by touch, working in close flocks.

When a Redshank stalks across the mud-flats, the protruding tails of the *corophium* shrimps disappear across the 8-cm strip of the bird's path. Five minutes later only half the shrimps have reappeared and, because of the lowered density of prey, the next Redshank takes three times as long as its predecessor to find food. This emphasizes the importance of the birds' being well-spaced when feeding.

One wader more likely to be seen on shingle beaches than on mud-flats is the Turnstone. Named with unusually simple accuracy, they really do turn stones by sliding their bills beneath pebbles and flicking them over to reveal prey such as sandhoppers. They will also use their bills to roll back the bright green alga *enteromorpha* to reveal prey or dig into the sand to find prey. All these feeding techniques appear to be 'lucky dips', but once the prey is discovered it is taken by sight, as are the Laver Spire Shells taken from the surface of the beach.

Turnstones are opportunist feeders and will even eat carrion. They have been recorded as feeding on dead sheep in Somerset, the remains of a wolf in Canada and, a delight to ornithologists with a penchant for the macabre, five were seen feeding on a human corpse on the Anglesey coast. In each case, the observers were at pains to note that the birds were feeding on the flesh and not on sandhoppers that happened to be on or under the carcase.

Although most of the migrants that pass through western Europe feed on tidal flats, rocky shores are still worth examining, because many species may also search for food among the seaweed and rock-pools, and Purple Sandpipers are specialists in feeding on rocky shores, running very quickly over seaweed and rocks uncovered by the tide to snap at small invertebrates, such as sea-slaters which have flattened bodies and look rather like woodlice. These sandpipers are rapid feeders, locating their prey by sight. Where they are feeding affects the speed at which they find food. In zones of mussels and seaweeds they take almost a minute to find ten items while in the more open barnacle zone they take only seventeen seconds to find ten items.

Turnstones use their short, comparatively stout bills to hammer open barnacles. They will also dislodge winkles and use the tip of their bills to winkle the animal from its shell. Occasionally they will probe sea anemones and suck out the remains of the anemone's last meal. They also use a cocked head, stone-turning posture to dislodge limpets, sliding their bills beneath the edge of the shell to prise it clear of the rock.

Oystercatchers have a different technique, but while they can successfully hammer the limpet (*Patella aspersa*) from a rock, they have no success with another species, *Patella vulgata*, which has a different shape. The hammering Oystercatcher attacks *aspersa* by aiming blows at the right-hand side where the horseshoe-shaped attachment ends and is weakest. If successful, it either dislodges the limpet or smashes through its shell and sucks out the contents. The other species of limpet is thicker and rounder, which it makes it difficult to identify the weak point. Oystercatchers soon learn to differentiate between the species and ignore *vulgata*.

Curlews are skilful probers, fully inserting their bills in the mud but they will also jab at the surface of mud, inserting their bills partially. They also hunt by sight and will take small crabs by pecking and grabbing them beneath the surface of water. Inland, at their breeding grounds on moorland and wet-meadows, Curlews will pick insects and other invertebrates from the ground or from plants. Sometimes, a bird standing on the ground will snap at flying insects.

When conditions make probing difficult for Woodcocks they will turn over animal droppings and leaves to reveal invertebrates beneath them. They will also pick items from the surface, particularly when feeding on seeds and berries.

The Common Sandpiper is largely insectivorous, catching flying insects that it locates by sight. It stalks insects with head held low to pick them from the ground, crevices, low vegetation and the droppings of farm animals. In its winter quarters in Africa, it has been seen foraging for insects and ectoparasites on the backs of hippotami and crocodiles. The large eyes and acute hearing enable the Stone Curlew to catch nocturnal insects. Flying moths are chased and caught by the Stone Curlew jumping into the air. Another compratively short-legged wader, the Terek Sandpiper, feeds on insects and other invertebrates which it hunts by walking forward with head held low.

Another wader which feeds on insects is the Ruff which eats beetles and other insects, such as grasshoppers, in wet grassland, walking steadily like a redshank and pecking at the surface. It has been seen following the plough and taking invertebrates from the newly turned soil. Ruffs also take flying insects and wade in water to take insects from the surface.

Several waders often flutter into the air after flying insects, but one, the Collared Pratincole, feeds like a swallow catching flying insects in the air. It is most active in the morning and evening and hunts in flocks. Unlike swallows, though, pratincoles also hunt insects on foot, dashing after them and leaning forward or leaping up to catch them. Another inland wader, the Cream-coloured Courser, is also insectivorous, but it hunts on foot, often in small flocks. It uses the dash-and-pause technique to peck at insects on the ground. Even larger grasshoppers and mantids are swallowed whole.

Because it had been absent for almost one hundred years from England as a breeding bird, the Avocet was the subject of concentrated research into its feeding requirements when it returned to breed in the 1940s. Its initial strongholds were Minsmere Levels and Havergate Island, both areas of reclaimed wet pasture which were flooded during World War II, thus creating ideal conditions for Avocets.

Both of these areas on the Suffolk coast came under the management of the Royal Society for the Protection of Birds. During the 1960s and 1970s, RSPB staff carried out extensive research into the Avocet's feeding habits, in order to manage the levels and salinity of

A pair of Collared Pratincoles catch flying insects in flight, a feeding technique for which they have similar adaptations to swallows.

the water to provide the conditions that produce high levels of the invertebrates on which Avocets feed.

Three main feeding techniques were identified. One of these is sight-feeding, picking insects and larvae from the surface of the water or the mud, moving slowly forward in an upright position with its up-turned bill held almost horizontal and suddenly thrusting its head forward with bill open to snatch prey. Avocets wintering on the Tamar Estuary between Devon and Cornwall swallow between 23 and 42 times per minute, which suggests that their food is very small. The other methods it employs are scything and stirring with the bill, both of which locate the food by touch.

Aquatic insects are among the prey of the closely related Black-winged Stilts. They snatch beetles from the surface, immerse their heads beneath the water to take dragonfly nymphs from below the surface and catch flying insects as they land.

Avocets have three main feeding methods: picking at the surface of the mud or water, scything with the bill to locate food by touch, and stirring in shallow water.

Spotted Redshanks hunt fish and aquatic insects by sight (as well as probing the mud for bottom-living invertebrates). Greenshanks use a dash-and-lunge technique to hunt fish and will also chase fish by dashing after them with bill half-submersed. They have been seen to hunt co-operatively in small flocks with Spotted Redshanks walking side-by-side and feeding continuously.

Feeding and swimming

Although their feet are not webbed, many waders can swim. Several do so habitually. The most frequent swimmers are the phalaropes, which have lobed feet to help them. They do feed more conventionally, wading and walking to pick prey from the water-surface, from mud or from plants. When swimming, Red-necked Phalaropes pick insects from the surface or, lunging forward, from just beneath the surface. Sometimes they will up-end, but they do not keep their heads under-water for as long as ducks do. Insects will be taken from plants emerging from the water and may be seized in flight with a fluttering dart from the surface. Red-necked Phalaropes will spin rapidly, bringing items of food to the surface. They will also take advantage of food brought to the surface by other animals and will feed among grebes, ducks and Avocets. These small birds seem to be remarkably unafraid of other animals including, fortunately for birdwatchers, human beings.

Grey Phalaropes, known locally in parts of America as 'whalebirds', have been seen following shoals of fish and marine mammals to feed on food disturbed by them. When whales rest on the surface with their backs exposed, phalaropes will land on them to feed on the ectoparasites.

Other waders that take to the water include Ruffs, which may wade, until they are out of their depth and then swim in search of emerging midges. Spotted Redshanks often feed in teams, swimming together disturbing and catching shoals of fish.

Feeding by touch

Although several species of waders probe beneath the surface to feed, none seems to feed exclusively by touch. Some of these also pick food from the surface, probably locating the items by sight. Probing is not entirely inadvertent and sight is probably used to identify where to probe.

The stitching of the Dunlin is a typical probing action. It is very quick and often leaves a characteristic trail of closely spaced bill marks, usually in pairs and in straight or wavy lines.

With their long sensitive bills Snipes are highly efficient probers. They feed mainly at night in shallow water or wet mud. Minimal

Spinning rapidly, a Red-necked Phalarope disturbs aquatic insects and snatches them when they come to the surface.

time is spent moving in search of food, the bird preferring to stay on one spot and make up to a dozen probes by swivelling before moving on. The depth of the probe may be a few millimetres or to the total length of the bill (up to 7 cm). The probing action is a swift up-and-down movement, averaging eight probes per minute. Worms are extracted from the soil by retracting the tip of the bill and securing the worm with the tongue.

The slighter, smaller Jack Snipes feed by probing and by picking items from the surface. Like Snipes they feed mainly at night or at dusk. On soft wet ground in March, Jack Snipes were seen to stand and

RIGHT *The Icelandic race of Black-tailed Godwits are larger and have longer bills than those that breed elsewhere in Europe. These features demonstrate Bergmann's Rule that animals in cooler climates are larger than members of the same species in warmer climates and Allen's Rule that bills and other protuberances are shorter in cold climates.*

The Snipe's long bill enables it to probe deep into mud in search for invertebrates. The smaller Jack Snipe also probes and uses its shorter bill to take food from the surface.

tap the ground with slightly open bills, possibly to cause small insects called spring-tails to rise to the soil surface. Great Snipes feed in a similar fashion to Snipes, but it has been suggested that they take more items from the surface than Snipes and wintering birds in Zambia enter water less often, preferring to feed at the edges of pools.

The Woodcock is another long-billed wader which takes its food by probing. Since its preferred habitat is open woodland, it has no reason to wade and, therefore, has legs that are comparatively shorter than those of most other waders. It probes leaf-mould on the woodland floor for worms and insect larvae.

Woodcocks hunt in a characteristic fashion walking and probing on an experimental basis with each step. As the weight of the bird is

RIGHT *Curlews use their long bills to extract worms from below the surface, cockles from mud and crabs in shallow pools.*

transferred to the front foot, the bill is inserted into the soil for up to a third of its length (up to 8 cm). The daily intake of earthworms by the Woodcock is equivalent to its own weight (about 300 g). An earthworm is held in the bill as it is withdrawn and swallowed whole or in pieces having been broken up by blows from the bird's bill. Smaller prey items are drawn up the bill by suction. In spring insects, mainly larvae of flies and beetles, make up a large proportion of the Woodcocks' food.

Curlews feed almost entirely by day in a wide variety of habitats, exposed and covered intertidal flats, saltings and pastures, and use a variety of techniques. They peck at the surface, hunt crabs by sight and probe the surface. The depths of the probes vary from half to the whole of the bill being inserted. When probing, Curlews move their heads to change the angle and are able to extract and swallow a cockle without complete withdrawal of the bill. However, winkles, which it takes from the surface have harder shells and must first be smashed.

The largest wader in the Western Palearctic, the Curlew varies in size, the largest being a fifth larger than the smallest. The lengths of individual's bills also vary and this appears to have an effect on feeding habits. Males tend to have bills that are up to a tenth shorter than females'. Extensive studies of waders at Teesmouth by

Black-tailed Godwits feed in deeper water than Bar-tailed Godwits.

Pienkowski and others showed long-billed birds to feed mainly on the mud-flats, eating Rag Worms, while short-billed individuals fed on pastures, eating earthworms. Similar preferences have been recorded on the Waddenzee, where it was also recorded that on mud-flats the longer-billed birds concentrated on soft-shelled clams while the shorter-billed took Rag Worms, Lugworms and Sand Masons.

Godwits are the next largest waders in the region. They are vigorous probers in search of polychaete worms and bivalves. Their feeding activity is limited by the availability of food and by the number of birds feeding. Single Bar-tailed Godwits feed less rapidly than those in flocks. Flocking birds have a probing rate of more than once per second, taking up to two food items in a minute, while single birds make about 50 probes a minute and capture less than one food item per minute. Counting the rate of godwits' probing can be difficult with the human eye so cine film has been used to make accurate assessments.

Female Bar-tailed Godwits have bills which may be a third longer than those of the males. The greater bill length gives females greater opportunities for feeding and they can feed in deeper water than the males, which tend to feed nearer the shoreline. The differences may help to reduce competition when there are large numbers in relation to available feeding areas.

Black-tailed Godwits have a more leisurely action, but they still manage up to 36 probes a minute. They also show a preference for

feeding in deeper water than Bar-tailed Godwits, which are altogether stockier and prefer to feed at the tide line or on the uncovered mud. They will also insert their bills in the mud and walk in a circle. In addition to feeding by touch they also hunt by sight.

Not all touch-feeders probe the surface. Purple Sandpipers find food by touch when searching for items in crevices in the rocks. The 'shanks will all feed in shallow water and are active hunters of swimming insects and small fish, but they will also probe the bottom for organisms such as hoverfly larvae.

Avocets use their fine, upturned bill to catch their swimming animal food in deep water with a forward and upward pecking action or by scything in shallow water or wet mud by swinging the head from side-to-side so that water is drawn through the bill and prey located by touch. Scything Avocets may work in groups in long lines.

ADAPTATIONS FOR FEEDING

Smaller prey can be sucked up through the bills of waders while they are still probing, but larger animals must be grasped between the mandibles, withdrawn from burrows and swallowed. To be able to grip its food at the tip of its bill, the latter must be flexible. Because its upper mandible is flexible, a wader can open the tip of its bill without having to open the base of the bill. This ability is less well developed in the shorter-billed plovers and thick-knees than in other waders and is best developed in curlews and snipes. These long-billed probers have highly sensitive bill-tips in order to be able to feel their unseen food.

The longer the wader's bill, the deeper it can probe the ground in search of food. But a long bill has a disadvantage in cold climates because of heat loss. Thus, bills and other protuberances are shorter within species in colder climates (Allen's Rule). Another rule, which is related to heat-loss, is Bergmann's Rule, in which members of the same species are larger in cooler climates than in warmer climates. The Icelandic race of Black-tailed Godwits demonstrates both rules by being larger and having shorter bills than fellow members of the species elsewhere in Europe.

The ways in which waders tackle their food subjects their bills to a variety of forces as the birds probe, peck, sweep, hack and lift. Great pressure is exerted across the bill as it is pushed into the soil. To reduce this pressure the bird rapidly quivers its head to enlarge the hole as it probes.

The sight-feeding plovers and thick-knees have short bills and large large eyes. The Stone Curlew, which is a twilight and night-time feeder, has very large eyes. Woodcocks also have crepuscular feeding habits and large eyes, but their solitary feeding and probing habit makes

The large eyes of the Stone Curlew help it to see and catch moths in the twilight and at night.

them vulnerable to surprise by predators. The eyes of Woodcocks and snipes are placed on the sides of the head to allow binocular vision backwards as well as forwards.

For birds that are solitary and spend long periods with their heads down backward vision is an important precaution against predators. By contrast, the plovers' eyes are positioned to enable good, forward binocular vision needed for finding food by sight. To overcome the consequent vulnerability to predation they form flocks which increases the chances of the presence of a predator being detected

The down-curved bills of Curlews and Whimbrels allow them a combination of trial probing and visual search. The Cream-coloured Courser has a shortish, slightly down-curved bill, a feature found in several species which feed on large insects. This may also allow the birds to follow more easily the U-shaped burrows of Lugworms

A bill that is curved upwards, such as the Avocet's, enables a wader to pursue active prey in shallow water with a sweeping movement. The smaller, slightly up-turned bill of the Turnstone has

The head of this Woodcock shows three adaptations to its habit of probing for food in poor light. The upper mandible of its long bill is flexible, which allows it to grasp worms with the tip of its bill without opening the bill completely. Its large eyes help it to see better at night and are positioned so that it can see backwards and spot predators when its head is down as it feeds.

a different function and is an adaptation that helps the bird to flick over stones and pebbles.

Heaviest of bills among waders are the Oystercatchers'. Their bills are hefty, but they are subjected to enormously heavy wear. They are used in a number of ways: to prise cockles from the mud, to knock mussels from their anchorage, to stab into and prise open

RIGHT *The different bill-shapes of waders have evolved to help them exploit a wide range of feeding opportunities. The Red-necked Phalarope picks insects from the water surface with its fine, pointed bill. The Cream-coloured Courser uses its shortish, down-curved bill to catch large insects. The slightly up-turned bill of the Turnstone helps it to live up to its name. The curved bill of the Curlew allows it to explore a greater area with one probe.*

The shape of an Oystercatcher's bill can give a clue to its feeding specialization. The bills of those that hammer open mussels through the weak points in their shells become worn and chisel-ended, those that hammer at the point where the mussel's shell-closing muscle is located have square-ended bills, and the probers have pointed bills.

bivalves, and to smash shells. Individuals have different techniques for dealing with mussels. The stabber forces its bill between the two valves of the shell and and slices through the larger of the two muscles which hold them together. The hammerers fall into two groups. The 'ventral hammerer' specializes in taking a mussel, wedging firmly and battering at the weak points on the shell to make a hole large enough to insert the bill and cut the muscle. Sight is important in selecting those mussels with weaker shells and the Oystercatchers select those that are dark brown rather than black and with few barnacles growing on them. The 'dorsal hammerer' selects its victims in the mussel-bed by tapping the shells and then hammering hard at the point where the shell-closing muscle is located in order that the two valves fall apart.

The horny covering of the bills of hammering Oystercatchers become very worn and the pointed ends can be square with wear. Such is the wear that the bills must continue to grow rapidly, in order to be renewed. This is unique among waders. At a rate of 0.4 mm per day, the growth is three times faster than that of human fingernails.

Among wintering Oystercatchers, there are three main bill-shapes: pointed, chisel-shaped and blunt. The pointed bills seem to be in greater proportions among females and juveniles and indicate stabbers, while the chisel-shaped bills belong to ventral hammerers and the blunt belong to dorsal hammerers. Stabbers have a slower feeding rate than hammerers and must supplement their diets by probing mud for worms. In the breeding season, when some Oystercatchers switch from shore feeding to inland feeding, the shape of their bills changes. Experiments with captive Oystercatchers have shown that the bill-shapes of hammerers, fed on a diet exclusively of Lugworms, will change from chisel-shaped to pointed within ten days.

Long legs enable waders to extend their search for food into deeper water, but those with long legs must have correspondingly long necks and bills with which to reach food when on land. Red-necked Phalaropes, which which spend much of their time swimming, have partially lobed feet. Sanderlings find food by sight, running across the mud at the tide's edge like mechanical toys. They have no hind toe, which enables them to move faster.

In most species of waders, the wingshapes have evolved in terms of the distances they travel rather than as an aid to feeding. But the pratincoles, which feed on flying insects, have long, pointed wings and, by the standards of other waders, long tails which are also forked. These adaptations give them the speed and manoeuvrability necessary to catch prey in flight.

THE PROBLEMS OF FINDING FOOD

The huge numbers of waders which winter in tidal areas have to contend with an environment that is continually changing. Each change presents different problems for finding food.

As the tide varies, so does the depth of the invertebrates on which waders feed. Crustacea and polychaete worms are closer to the surface of the mud when the tide is beginning to cover or uncover it. Smaller waders, such as Dunlins and Sanderlings, follow the tide's edge and larger species, such as Bar-tailed Godwits and Curlews, feed in the shallower areas about to be uncovered or just covered by the tide.

Weather also has an effect on prey. When it gets colder the prey species burrow deeper and, since they do not breed during the winter, their numbers decrease. Thus, when the birds most need food to provide energy to keep warm, the food itself is at its most difficult to find.

Research into the wintering behaviour of Grey Plovers on the north-east coast of England showed that birds caught less prey in the coldest weather. Although they gathered at the areas of highest prey density on Lindisfarne, they maintained their individual distance from each other and as the weather became colder, the individual distances increased. Smith's and Evans' studies at Lindisfarne showed that when the temperature dropped below 3 °C, Lugworms became less active and the Bar-tailed Godwits' success in finding food diminished.

Wind also adds to the problems faced by waders. Onshore winds can hold back the incoming tide reducing the available feeding time especially in enclosed basins or at neap tides where there is only a small difference in depth (1–2 m) between high and low water. As wind increases waders lose heat, their prey burrows deeper and the wind cause ripples in the water, making finding food by sight more difficult. Purple Sandpipers, which are daytime feeders at the tide's edge on rocky shores, are vulnerable to strong winds. They therefore seek sheltered feeding places. They fly from the shore to nearby damp pastures and machair, where they feed by picking food items from the ground and even probing the earth in search of food.

The difficulties encountered by waders feeding around the coasts of north-western Europe make them very mobile in their choice of feeding sites. Thus, when conditions in one area are inhospitable they will move to another where feeding is less difficult. However, some waders are faithful to their wintering sites and only move when feeding is impossible.

Periodically, the food supplies fail and numbers of waders drop. Recently, during the winter of 1992–93, unusually high numbers of Oystercatchers were found dead around the Wash. Thanks to the Birds of Estuaries Enquiry, organized by the British Trust for Ornithology, numbers of this species wintering on the Wash had been monitored for the previous 21 years. Having reached a peak of over 45,000 in 1988 there were only 12,000 in January 1993. The dead birds were of all ages and included three that had been ringed in 1967 and 1968.

As we have seen, Oystercatchers' feeding preferences are shown in the shapes of their bills and since the birds found dead included individuals of each bill-shape it seemed unlikely that the deaths were linked to the lack of one particular prey species, but was more likely to be the result of something affecting the overall food supply. However, it did seem clear that no other bird species was affected, which suggested that pollution was not the cause.

Because of their commercial value, populations of cockles and mussels, the main prey of Oystercatchers, are monitored by the Ministry of Agriculture, Fisheries and Food and the Eastern Sea Fisheries Committee. Their information shows that populations of these molluscs varies greatly on the Wash. In some years young do not become established in large numbers. The dynamics of the mussel are still unclear, but it is known that the best years for young are those when there are high numbers of adults. The last good year for mussels was 1986 and fears have been expressed that it may be many years before the populations recover.

On the other hand, more is known about cockles, whose young become established in greatest numbers in years following severe winter weather and fewer adults, because the adults eat many of the young spat. Because 1992 was a good year for the establishment of young cockles, the future for the Oystercatchers of the Wash does not look so bleak.

As well as being low in numbers the cockles and mussels had less meat on them than normal. No one has discovered why this should be so, but its effect on Oystercatchers has been serious. Less prey means the birds must spend more energy searching for food that has less bulk, which means searching for more food, which means greater expenditure of energy. The result is that the birds may expend greater energy in finding food than the food provides.

WHERE WADERS FEED

With one or two exceptions, waders feed in the open. Their natural feeding environment is, for much of the year, uncovered tidal flats and the shallow water at the edge of the tide. This means that some species may be deterred from feeding close to sea walls because of the limitation on their all-round vision.

There is a clear link between the densities of prey and the numbers of birds. Thus, Oystercatchers in Strangford Lough in Ulster are densest where the cockles are densest. John Goss-Custard found that the density of Redshanks on the Ythan Estuary in Scotland was related to the density of the crustacean *Corophium volutator*. At lower densities, the populations of predators and prey is proportional, but the birds reach a population plateau before the crustaceans. At eight sites investigated by Goss-Custard on the Essex and south Suffolk coast, the average winter densities from November to March of Curlews and Redshanks could be correlated to food density.

TIMES OF FEEDING

While some waders feed only during the day and others largely during the night, many feed both during day and night depending on the need for food. In mid-winter in tidal areas, night-time feeding may be as important as day-time feeding for some species.

For those that usually find their prey by sight, feeding at night is difficult because even when the moon is full their ability to see their prey is limited. This disadvantage is probably balanced by the increased activity of their invertebrate prey which means that there are more individual food items available.

Investigations into the behaviour of Dunlins on the Severn Estuary showed that, while similar numbers of pellets were found at night-time high-tide roosts as at day-time roosts, the contents of the pellets was different. Night-time pellets contained fewer remains of Rag Worms and more of tellins and Laver Spire Shells than day-time pellets. Because the Dunlins spent more time at the night-time roosts, the similar amounts of pellets might suggest that a smaller amount of food is taken at night.

The Redshanks studied by Goss-Custard on the Ythan Estuary spent more of each 24-hour period feeding in winter than in spring or autumn and less than half of their food was obtained during daylight. The increased feeding activity was probably due to a combination of the increased needs for food in cold weather, the reduction in the size of the food items, their increasing scarcity and the length of the nights.

Like many birds that hunt larger flying insects, Collared Pratincoles are most active at dawn and dusk. Stone Curlews forage from dusk to

When there is a cold wind it is difficult for Grey Plovers to find food. Those that maintain territories in creeks are sheltered from the wind and able to feed for longer periods.

dawn, hunting the invertebrates which are active in darkness. The prey is heard or seen several metres away and stalked in a heron-like manner and grasped with a rapid stabbing motion.

When wintering in Israel, Dotterels feeds at night or in the early morning on insects and spiders. During the day, they stand motionless in flocks in the Golan and the western Negev desert. This habit makes them very difficult to see and Uzi Paz suggests that they may, therefore, be more numerous in Israel than records suggest.

FEEDING TERRITORIES

Species that feed in close flocks do not maintain feeding territories, but they do keep individual distance from each other. Those waders that feed at some distance from each other do not feed territorially.

Aggression between feeding Oystercatchers often involves one stealing food from another.

The extensive investigations by Townshend, Dugan and Pienkowski at Teesmouth into the behaviour of Grey Plovers has shown that there were two types of territorial behaviour by different individuals. Using colour rings to identify individuals, they discovered that there were some which defended fixed feeding sites. Each individual maintained a fixed site for months and these territories were deep creeks which provided shelter when feeding in strong winds.

The other individuals fed without a long-term territory and were widely distributed across the feeding grounds, but occasionally they defended feeding sites for a few hours, days or even weeks. The temporarily defended territories were often on the sandier, more quickly drying areas where the prey was not available for very long. In the wetter sites, the density of plovers was higher and these short-term territories were rare. Because the feeding area was open, winds had a detrimental effect on their feeding. Once the wind reached 46 kph the Grey Plovers stopped feeding.

Short-term territoriality seemed to occur mainly in October and during January and February, which coincided with both peaks in population size and the coldest weather. There is a clear advantage to individuals in maintaining prey numbers and in excluding other birds which might disturb prey and make it more difficult to find.

Holders of long-term territories spent time dispelling intruders when they could have been finding food and they were at more risk from foxes. At night, territory-holders were obliged to feed within their territories to prevent them being usurped, while the others were able to move to areas where the larger Rag Worms were active. On the other hand the long-term territories maintained stocks of prey and enabled the territory-holder to make selective use of patches of prey, while the shelter of the deep creeks made feeding possible when the wind in open areas was more than 46 kph.

Studies of Oystercatchers on the Exe estuary suggest that they do not defend feeding territories in the mussel beds, but that aggression displays were attempts to steal food. On the Ythan, too, most of the aggression involved stealing food. It seems that some individuals are particularly aggressive, attacking other birds at an average of five-minute intervals at low tide. The time lost in aggression seems to have been more than compensated for by the individuals' success as pirates. Some obtained up to 60 per cent of their food by stealing.

FLOCKING AND ROOSTING

Flocking is a feature of wader behaviour outside the breeding season. A few species, such as Common Sandpipers, migrate singly or in small groups, but form flocks on arrival at their sub-Saharan wintering grounds. Some, such as Black-winged Stilts and Avocets, breed in loose colonies and Collared Pratincoles, which feed on flying insects, nest in close enough colonies to feed like terns or hirundines in flocks. Generally, though, it is for migration and wintering that wader flocking is most important.

BENEFITS AND COSTS OF FORMING FLOCKS

Forming flocks concentrates birds in far fewer places than if they were widely dispersed as individuals over a wide area. This gives them protection from predators, which have less opportunities to find widely spaced flocks than well-spread individuals. Against this, an individual bird has a greater chance of being overlooked by a predator than a flock does.

Once in a group an individual bird does have the security of safety in numbers. In the presence of large numbers of other birds the odds against an individual being taken by a predator are raised. The multiplication of pairs of eyes and ears increases the chances of detecting a predator before it can spring a surprise attack. Since surprise is an important element of most predators' hunting techniques, any factor that reduces the chance of surprise increases the odds in favour of the prey.

Quantities appear to confuse a predator, especially in a tight flock of waders, which wheels and suddenly splits into several smaller flocks. The value of flocks to prey is shown by studies of pike, which were less successful when preying on shoals of minnows than on individuals. Merlins on the east coast of North America were found to be least successful against medium-sized flocks of waders and it was these flocks that were least likely to be attacked. A tight flock in flight may also be a deterrent to a raptor because of the risk of damage in a collision with birds other than the intended victim.

Being vigilant for predators is time-consuming and time spent on watch is time that might be spent feeding. Therefore, when a flock feeds some individuals are 'sentries', allowing others to feed faster than they would if they were also on the alert for predators. Studies

Dunlins in tight, medium-sized, tight-flying flocks appear to be safer than those in larger, looser flocks.

of geese have shown that the number of alert individuals does not increase proportionately to the size of the flock, which means that more members of the larger flocks are able to spend more time feeding. At a roost, larger flocks appear to give more security to individual birds, allowing them to 'peek' less often than those in smaller flocks (*see* page 87–9).

Although flocking does protect waders from predators, they are more vulnerable to predation in larger flocks. At a distance, a single bird or even a small flock might escape the notice of a patrolling raptor, but a large flock is noticeable at a distance and may attract a predator.

On the ground, feeding or roosting, waders are vulnerable to both birds of prey and to ground predators, such as foxes and stoats. In the air they are safer: only birds of prey are a threat and a flying flock presents a moving target. However, despite the advantage of taking to the air, feeding waders which have been warned by one of the 'sentries' of an approaching predator, may not take off immediately because the longer they stay, the longer they can feed. The speed of their reactions may depend on the species of the predator. For example, sandpipers are able to delay response to an approaching Merlin because, once they are airborne, they can outfly the falcon. However, if they misjudge the delay, it may mean that a sandpiper on the edge of the flock will be a victim.

Wintering waders are an important source of food for individual raptors. At a coastal site in California, intensively studied by Page and Whitacre, one female Merlin took 122 sandpipers and 12 other vertebrates between 21 September and 28 February 1972. She would attack but not strike larger waders. Over half the diet of a Short-eared Owl at the same site was birds.

The defensive response of waders to predators varies between species. When a Kestrel passes over a Ringed Plover roost, the birds scatter flying low and fast, in all directions. The reaction of Dunlins is to climb hard in a tight flock, circling the roost until the Kestrel has passed. Dunlins will flee from passing crows, but Oystercatchers react by attacking the crows.

The chances of individual birds finding food are increased in flocks because of the increased number of pairs of eyes searching. As we have seen, in some cases, such as Spotted Redshanks, small flocks may work as teams, disturbing small fish and other aquatic animals for mutual benefit: this is an example of co-operative feeding only slightly less dramatic than group fishing by White Pelicans. Because prey is patchily distributed in the mud of estuaries and flats, the greater the flock the greater the likelihood of a foraging bird or group of foraging birds discovering one of the patches with a higher density of prey, which other members of the flock can exploit.

When roosting in flocks, birds appear to able to pass and receive information about likely sources of food. How the roost acts as an information centre is not clear. It is possible that the birds that have had a successful day's foraging are noticeably fatter or demonstrate some other evidence of their success and less successful foragers follow them next day. The aerobatics performed by waders about to roost may also have an information-passing function.

It is when flocks reach their largest numbers that the costs of flocking become most apparent when feeding. For sight-feeding waders, closeness to other birds may be a disadvantage. The proximity of feeding waders to each other depends on the species and on factors such as the species of prey, the method of feeding and the time of day.

Roosting Knots pack tightly together, while larger waders, such as Curlews and Oystercatchers, allow several birds' lengths between individuals, and Dunlins form looser feeding flocks.

During the day, Redshanks feeding on *corophium* shrimps on mud-flats, which they find by sight, are well-separated from each other to prevent wasteful competition. At night, however, the same birds will pack together in tight flocks and feed on small snails, which they find by touch.

When the flocks are very large, individual Oystercatchers and sandpipers become aggressive to each other, wasting time on rivalry when they might be feeding. When two Ringed Plovers are feeding too close they may distract each other and, having disturbed their prey, accidentally allow it to take cover. Similarly, Curlews feeding at high density will take less food than those with plenty of individual distance.

Roosting waders will huddle closely. The closeness of individuals can give clues to their identity: Knots pack tightly, Dunlins more loosely and the larger waders – Oystercatchers, Curlews and Bar-tailed Godwits – have several birds' lengths between them.

The species of waders which fly in close flocks have wing-bars, which may have a function in coordinating the positions of individuals in flight. As Peter Ferns has pointed out, Curlews, which form loose flocks, lack wing-bars, as do the solitary Greenshanks and Green Sandpipers.

TIDAL ROOSTS

A roost creates a micro-climate at the centre of which the wind speed is less and the temperature is warmer. In flocks of roosting Redshanks the warmest places are taken by the adults, and the juveniles are forced to the windward side. The birds in the flock all face in the same direction, head-to-wind, so that their plumage is minimally ruffled. In terms of energy-conservation the flock offers no advantage to the juveniles, which means that it must have another value, perhaps in finding food and protection from predators, which tips the balance in favour of being a member of a flock.

Once the tide covers the flats to a depth that makes them inaccessible to the feeding waders, they begin to return to their high-tide roosts. For about two-fifths of each tide around the British coasts the flocks of waders cannot feed. With two tides each day wintering waders may spend up to nine hours at the roost or commuting between roosts and feeding grounds. The roosts may be

Flying flocks may be recognized at a distance by their behaviour: Knots fly in tighter flocks, flocks of Curlews are strung out, Grey Plovers fly in small groups of about six and Oystercatchers often fly in lines.

close to the feeding grounds but they are often traditional sites and may be up to 15 km from the feeding grounds.

Generally, the order in which the species return to their roosts is the same and their behaviour can be a clue to identifying them from a distance. Oystercatchers, which spend longer at the roost than other species, form compact roosts on the mud-flats up to an hour before other species arrive. They fly in tight flocks to roost. Within an hour they are followed by Curlews and Bar-tailed Godwits, straggling in ragged 'V' formations or strung out in long lines. Grey Plovers then make for the roost in small groups of about half-a-dozen birds. At about the same time Knots, having formed into close flocks on the mud-flats, fly to the roost. The smaller, tide-edge feeders, Dunlins, Sanderlings and Ringed Plovers, move back with the tide and stay until about an hour before high tide. On the low neap tides they will remain strung out along the shore and may not visit the roost at all.

Roosting flocks may be a mixture of all the species which feed on the flats, but some are single-species flocks. Curlews and Redshanks show the greatest tendency to roost in single-species flocks but other species such as Ringed Plovers, Turnstones, Black-tailed Godwits and Oystercatchers will also do so. In some areas flocks of Oystercatchers will return to the same feeding and roosting areas year after year, apparently keeping themselves away from the areas of neighbouring flocks. During the breeding season non-breeders will still cling to the winter roosts, but obviously the numbers will be fewer than in winter.

Aerial surveys have shown where species prefer to roost. Bar-tailed Godwits, for example, are always the closest to the sea and some may roost below high-water mark with their feet in the sea. Curlews and Oystercatchers roost on salt-marshes.

The aerobatics of waders before they settle to roost are among the great bird spectaculars. These displays are almost always performed by flocks of a single species. The stars are Knots, but godwits, Dunlins and Curlews also perform. Watching the movements of a tight-flying flock of Knots is like watching a constantly changing abstract sculpture, given added depth by the flashing effect of the pale undersides and darker backs of the birds as they turn. The function of these wheeling flocks is the subject of debate. The constant movement would certainly confuse a predator, but, since the birds do it when there are no predators present, there may be another reason for it. It has been suggested that it is a form of display, from which birds can ascertain their numbers and some can move on to another area where food might be more abundant, but for waders to be able to do this they would have to know the numbers at other nearby roosts. When wintering passerines gather to roost, they fly around together, if less spectacularly than waders, before settling and I have seen migrating Painted Lady butterflies behaving in a similar manner in Israel. Perhaps such behaviour has a function in reinforcing identification of species or individuals.

Flying in a flock requires instantaneous reactions if the birds are not to crash into each other. Each flock of waders swirling above an estuary is demonstrating synchronization than cannot be approached by human beings. While synchronized human activities can barely be described as vital, for flying waders it is an integral part of their lives. Each bird has to be acutely aware of its immediate neighbours, those with which it is most likely to collide, and they are able to alter course very rapidly. Contact-calls, alarm calls, wing-bars and tail flashes play a part in warning other members of the flock of changes in direction.

When flying flocks of waders land, there is considerable movement as the birds settle. Oystercatchers, Grey Plovers, Curlews, Redshanks and godwits quickly settle to sleep or rest, while Dunlins, Sanderlings and Ringed Plovers feed wherever possible. All species spend part of the high-tide period preening.

The last to arrive at the roost, Dunlins, Sanderlings and Ringed Plovers, are the first to return to feed on the shore, following the tide as it ebbs. The Knots leave to form sub-roosts on the flats before starting to feed. The next arrivals back on the flats are Bar-tailed Godwits, which remain in sub-roosts for about 30 minutes before moving to the tide-edge. Curlews, on the other hand, fly straight to the mud and begin to feed. Redshanks feed close to the salt-marsh and along the channels in the mud-flats. Finally, the Oystercatchers leave the roost up to an hour after the other waders.

Disturbance is a problem for roosting waders. Those from the Dee estuary which roost on Hilbre Island may spend up to three hours on the wing when they would normally be roosting. However, not all human interference with the waders' environment is detrimental. At Musselburgh Power Station on the south shore of the Firth of Forth, pits dug for ash-dumping created shallow lagoons which inadvertently provided a high-quality roosting site for waders. The numbers grew from 800 to 7000 birds and included Golden Plovers, which had previously roosted inland, and Bar-tailed Godwits, Knots, Curlews and Dunlins, which had previously had a 30-km round trip to their roosts.

Away from the coast, flocks of Lapwings and Golden Plovers roost together. Golden Plovers may sleep during the day and feed at night, particularly when there is a full moon, but since they feed at night when it is overcast the link with the full moon may not purely be the availability of light.

When some coastal winterers return to their breeding grounds they will roost communally until they nest. Painted Snipes roost singly on the ground during day-light hours, leaving cover to feed from dusk to dawn. The gregarious Collared Pratincoles, by contrast, roost on the ground in the open in flocks, showing a marked preference for closely-cropped grassland. They are least active during the heat of the midday sun between 11 a.m. and 3 p.m. when they roost. They will feed during the night in clear moonlight.

FLOCKS OF PLOVERS AND LAPWINGS

Nesting in scattered groups of 3–20 pairs, Sociable Plovers are semi-colonial breeders, but their sociability comes to the fore in Russia and Kazakhstan when they disperse at the end of the breeding season to form flocks of hundreds of birds. Many migrate in smaller flocks, or singly, or in flocks with other waders.

In winter in Northern Europe, Lapwings and Golden Plovers often flock together with Black-headed Gulls on farmland. Plover flocks have been divided by Barnard and Thompson into four categories: foraging, pre-foraging, post-foraging and roosting. Some birds in each flock category perform functions associated with the other types.

Foraging flocks of Golden Plovers, Lapwings and Black-headed Gulls will feed together in winter in old pasture.

In a foraging flock at least 90 per cent of the birds are hunting for or eating prey and they are well-spaced, with the individuals facing in a variety of directions. Golden Plovers usually feed with Lapwings, but Lapwings are often recorded feeding in single-species flocks. When Black-headed Gulls are present the flocks are almost invariably mixed flocks of plovers and Lapwings.

Having moved from roosts on ploughed fields soon after dawn, plovers and Lapwings build up pre-foraging flocks on sown fields usually containing a few foragers. The inactive birds all face into the wind like roosting birds. These flocks are often mixed but the Golden Plovers are more likely to be in single-species flocks than when they are foraging.

After feeding, and up to two hours before dusk, the plovers move once more to sown fields. Here, they behave similarly to pre-foraging flocks but with fewer individuals feeding. Golden Plovers are found in mixed post-foraging flocks only and the proportion of gulls is lower.

It is usually as dusk approaches that the roosting flocks build up on ploughed fields. Lapwings and plovers usually split into separate roosts in different parts of the fields.

The plovers show a preference for feeding in old pasture and this is probably an extension of their grassland feeding in the breeding

season. The spreading conversion of grassland to arable in Northern Europe is a probable cause of the decline in plover populations.

The density of earthworms is highest in old pastures, and this attracts Lapwings either in single species or mixed-species flocks. Lapwings are used by Black-headed Gulls and Golden Plovers as indicators of the fields that are best for earthworms. The effect of this attention is that as the winter progresses the numbers of worms diminish, but their numbers recover faster on old pasture than on new. It appears that the birds allow earthworms numbers to recover by leaving the well-used pastures fallow.

For Black-headed Gulls the plovers and Lapwings may represent a source of food to be stolen. They are twice as successful in robbing Lapwings as in robbing Golden Plovers because the latter are more agile and swifter to react. Kleptoparasticism reduces the plovers' feeding efficiency which will also be affected by temperature, day-length and availability of food.

Among Lapwings, efficiency varies between individuals of different ages, sexes and competitive ability and, where efficency is low, the birds may continue to feed into the night.

Despite the fact that gulls steal their food, the relationship between the gulls and their victims may be commensal: the trade-off for the plovers is the gulls' alertness to predators.

PLUMAGE AND MOULT

To function efficiently, a bird must keep itself in the best possible condition. This includes feeding to provide both the energy to function and the warmth to survive the cold. Body temperature is also maintained by the feathers of birds, which provide protection against heat loss from the effects of winds and, in warmer climates, against overheating. Birds are unable to fly if they do not have flight feathers. In some species, such as Ruffs, feathers provide adornments that play an important part in courtship.

Feathers are intricate structures which provide weather-proofing and insulation. They are manoeuvrable by a series of muscles providing an effect, like the opening of louvres, for cooling the skin or maintaining the feathers. The wear and tear on them is heavy and they need to be maintained day-to-day and replaced at least annually.

All the feathers of a wader are renewed at least once a year and the body feathers of most species twice a year. The number of feathers on an individual bird varies between species, but differences between individual members of the same species is small. Information about the number of feathers in birds of individual species is scarce. Small sandpipers have about 4500 contour feathers.

Moulting is one of the most stressful regular events of a bird's life and extra food is needed to sustain the production of new feathers. It must take place when there is sufficient food, but it must not interfere with other major activities. Therefore, it generally happens before and after breeding in the spring and autumn. But as waders are generally migrants, moult and migration must both be fitted into the bird's life-cycle. The timing is very important and the period of moult varies between species, and can vary between sexes and ages within a species.

MOULT SEQUENCE

Wader chicks emerge from the egg covered with down. Gradually the down is replaced by contour feathers and within a few weeks the bird can fly. Generally some of the body feathers are replaced in a spring moult and all the feathers including the flight feathers are moulted in autumn. Thereafter, most waders undergo two annual moults, partially in the spring before breeding and completely in autumn.

Wader chicks are precocial, which means that when they hatch they are feathered, capable of feeding themselves and able to walk. The feathers begin to develop within the egg. The skin of the embryo develops pimples, known as 'feather germs', which subse-quently sink into the surface to create a cylindrical pit, known as a 'follicle', from which the feathers will grow. The plumage that covers a newly hatched wader is soft, natal down. These plumes are fluffy and much softer than the contour feathers which will replace them. This fluffiness is because of the structure of the feathers: the short quill is topped by soft barbs which can be moved in any direction. While the chick is still very small the main function of the down is to provide warmth. However, life on the ground is very hazardous for a small animal, even when protected by a parent. Its down, therefore, needs to be camouflaged so that it can merge into its surround-ings (*see* page 119).

Although traces of down remain for several weeks, at about seven days the first contour feathers begin to appear on the back and scapulars. They are stiffer, with long quills from which two vanes of interlocking barbs grow. The next contour feathers to appear are those on the breast and the wing coverts, followed by the primaries. Last to appear are the tail feathers and with them the birds fledge and can fly. Young Snipes are exceptional in that they can fly, albeit weakly, weakly before the tail feathers appear. The time taken to fledge varies between species and within species between sexes, but it ranges from between eighteen days in some Red-necked Phalaropes and 42 days in Curlews.

The primaries do not reach their full length for several weeks after fledging. In most waders these feathers remain for some eighteen months after fledging until their first autumn moult. Exceptions are the coursers and pratincoles. Cream-coloured Coursers start their first moult within a few weeks of fledging. Breeding begins early in the year in the warmer southern parts of the region and those chicks that fledge between March and May will moult completely over the next four months. This moult has three phases, starting with head, mantle and chest, followed by scapulars and most of the wing-coverts, and then with the tertials, tail-coverts, back and rump. It is complete by August at the earliest. The primaries take six months to be completely replaced, which means that the moult of the earliest hatching chicks has finished by the time the birds leave their

Curlews chicks emerge from the egg covered in down. The contour feathers begin to appear on the back and scapulars at about seven days. Next to appear are the breast feathers, followed by the wing coverts and primaries. Finally, at about 42 days, the tail feathers appear and the bird can fly.

First-winter Ringed Plovers can be recognized by the pale-edged mantle, scapulars and wing coverts.

breeding grounds towards the end of September. Those birds that have fledged later than early May suspend the moult of wing and body feathers in September and resume it after migration in late October and November.

Young Collared Pratincoles go through a complete post-juvenile moult which begins in August and early September. The moult is suspended for the autumn migration to sub-Saharan Africa. The moult is resumed in October when the winter quarters have been reached. The adults' moult is completed more quickly, with more feathers renewed before migration, and finished usually by December.

First-winter birds of most wader species can be recognized by their retention of some juvenile feathers and the distinctive pale-edged feathers of the post-juvenile plumage. For example, the pale buff margins to the scapulars and wing-coverts of first-winter Ringed Plovers create a scaly appearance.

After their partial autumn moult between August and December, young Oystercatchers can be identified by the brownish tinge to their upper parts, tertials and wing-coverts and by the buffish white upper tail coverts. The buff feather edges wear away quickly, but some remain on the inner wing-coverts and tail-coverts throughout the winter. The juvenile wing and tail feathers remain so that the tail band is finer than in the adults and the feathers are much more abraded than the adults'.

Slowly, during that first autumn, a white neck band develops, initially as a result of the black tips of the neck feathers wearing and subsequently as white feathers grow through. The white collar in first-winter birds is larger than in adults and the colour of legs, bills and eyes are different: the legs are grey, gradually turning pink; the bill is reddish at the base and dark towards the tip; the eyes are pale brownish red rather than the adult's black with red irises and the eye-ring is yellow, gradually turning to red.

During the first few months of Oystercatchers' second calendar year they undergo a partial moult of some scapulars, some tertials, some wing-coverts and often central tail feathers. In May or June they begin a complete moult, slightly earlier than the adults.

An adult and a first-winter Oystercatcher showing the differences in plumage, and the colours of the eyes, bills and legs.

Although Oystercatchers do not usually breed before their fourth year, breeding plumage is acquired in the spring of their third calendar year. From this moult the young birds follow the adult pattern with a partial pre-breeding moult between December and April, when the white collar is replaced with shining blue-black feathers and a full post-breeding moult between August and December.

POST-BREEDING MOULT

The full post-breeding moult is both stressful and time-consuming. The duration of the moult may vary within a species: Dunlins in the British Isles take about 60 days; in the Netherlands their moult takes 90–94 days; in Alaska it takes 70 days and in Morocco 100 days.

Where moult takes place before migration there have to be good food supplies and its duration tends be shorter. Purple Sandpipers begin their moult on Spitsbergen when they have finished rearing their young. The females begin first, because they leave the young in the charge of the males, and move to the coast. They begin to moult in the last ten days of July and the males generally start in the first ten days of August, but non-breeders or failed breeders may begin as early as 15 July. Birds on Spitsbergen take between 40 and 45 days to renew their flight feathers, but in other areas the moult may take longer and some birds will delay it until they reach their wintering grounds.

While some species of waders delay their moult until arrival at their wintering grounds, for some it is only postponed until they reach an appropriate place on their southward journey. The highly productive estuaries and flats of the North Sea provide an autumnal abundance of invertebrate food for moulting waders.

Some Dunlins may be in moult as they move south, tending to make shorter journeys between more staging posts than those which fly to north-west Africa, where they undergo their complete moult. Thus, some of the Dunlins that stop on the British coast pause long enough to stoke up for the journey southwards, but others, including Scandinavian and Russian breeders, stay in the Wash along with many Siberian Sanderlings for ten weeks, when they undergo a complete moult. These birds then move south-west from the Wash to the southern and south coasts of Britain and Ireland on their way to Africa, via France and Spain.

The Waddenzee is another moulting site for the Scandinavian and Russian Dunlins. On completion of their moult some of these birds

During a ten-week stay on the Wash, Sanderlings from Siberia undergo a complete post-breeding moult.

move westwards to the Wash to replace the birds on the way to Iberia. Some of the other Waddenzee birds follow the English Channel on their way to Spain and all points south.

Some Green Sandpipers arrive in Britain without having begun their moult, but begin to do so partially before moving south again. This accounts for the individuals and small flocks to be found on the shallow, inland water bodies in eastern and southern England in July and August.

Female Spotted Redshanks begin their post-breeding moult in June in their sub-Arctic breeding grounds, but suspend it when they begin to migrate south later in the month. Similarly, the males which migrate later in July, suspend their moult and resume it when they reach the temperate North Sea coasts. In Britain and the Netherlands, two groups of migrating Spotted Redshanks have been identified: the first tends to be comprised largely of females and non-breeders which have completed their moult by the time the second group arrives a month later still in their dark breeding plumage. The second group consists mainly of males and the young of the year.

PRE-BREEDING MOULT

The pre-breeding moult will produce those feathers that will play an important part in attracting members of the opposite sex. Among waders, breeding plumage is at its most exaggerated in Ruffs, the males of which moult into a breeding plumage between January and April. The colours of the breeding plumage are variable but it consists principally of black, blotched feathers on the breast and dark feathers on the back. This moult is followed by another partial moult in April when much of the plumage on the head, sides of the neck, chest, mantle and scapulars are replaced by the dramatic adornments which give the bird its name. There are so many variations in colours of the ruffs and ear-tufts that to find two birds that are similar is rare. At this stage the facial warts of Ruffs become exaggerated.

The magnificence of the Ruff does not last long. A complete moult begins in early June, before the males have moved far from the breeding grounds. It starts with the exaggerated ruff for which there is no longer a function once selection of mates is over. From the end of June to the beginning of August they begin to moult their primaries,

The pre-breeding moult of the male Ruff begins in January with dark blotched feathers on the breast and back. In April, the head, breast, head and neck feathers are replaced by the ruffs and head tufts and the facial warts become exaggerated. By June, the post-breeding moult begins. By September, many will have completed their moult.

starting with those nearest to the humerus and working outwards. For many Ruffs, the wings have moulted by mid-September and they have brand-new feathers for the southward journey. Those who have moulted only a few primaries by early September will probably suspend their moult and resume it on their arrival in Africa.

The pre-breeding moult in other species may produce less dramatic results, but colours of feathers become brighter in the males of many species and the female phalaropes and Dotterels. The colours of bills and legs become brighter, too.

Brood-patches

There is also a less glamorous function to pre-breeding moult in many species. It is to create brood-patches, which provide a way to transfer heat from the adult bird to the egg. In the pre-breeding moult, feathers are lost from a patch on the breast. The veins swell and move near the surface of the brood-patch. Brood-patches only develop in those birds that incubate. Thus, they are found in both sexes of Black-tailed Godwits, in female Ruffs and in male Red-necked Phalaropes.

COLOUR CHANGES

Colours of plumage may not always change as a result of moult. Wear and tear also contributes. Over the summer the chestnut-edged breeding plumage of Dunlins nesting in Britain wears away to produce a darker plumage. By contrast, the sun and salt breezes bleach the upperparts of Ringed Plovers and those nesting on coasts seem to be paler by July. The plumage of Greenshanks and, to a lesser extent, Redshanks turn darker through the summer because of darkening of the pigment in the feather quills and barbs. The individual feathers of Greenshanks darken from pale grey in April to dark brown in September. The cause is not known, but it has been suggested that it might be the result of oxidization of the materials in feathers.

COMFORT BEHAVIOUR

Between moults each wader must keep its 4000–5000 contour feathers in the best possible condition. The structure of a feather is an intricate arrangement of barbs and barbules growing from the quill, or rachis. This arrangement is based on the barbs and barbules hooking on to each other to make a firm, tough surface. If they become unhooked the feather surface is disrupted and the bird's insulation, flight and camouflage all become less efficient. It is important, therefore, that each bird cares for its plumage and prevents individual feathers becoming ragged by repairing any that have become disarrayed. To keep poumage in trim, feathers must be cleaned of foreign bodies and be waterproofed by oiling.

BATHING

The affinity of waders for water means that they have plenty of opportunity to bathe, immersing their heads and necks and flicking water on to their backs. The plumage is dampened rather than soaked and it may be that the main purpose is to make preening and oiling easier. To dry themselves they flick the excess water from their bodies.

OILING

Waders have an oil-gland on the rump which secretes a fatty oil with which a bird can waterproof its plumage, but it also has other properties. It has been suggested that the oil may contain antibiotics which counter fungal infections and that substances within it, when exposed to the sun, are converted to Vitamin D which is then ingested during preening or absorbed through the skin.

Oiling usually takes place after bathing and drying. The bird squeezes the nipple of the oil gland with the tip of its bill to obtain the oil, which it then spreads with its bill. With their long bills, waders do not have any great difficulty in oiling most of their feathers individually. However, there are parts of their heads and necks which their bills cannot reach and to oil these the birds must roll them against plumage that has already been oiled. With their long bills they can easily oil the underside of their primaries.

An Avocet preening in order to clean and rearrange its feathers.

PREENING

Preening is the climax of the sequence of bathing, drying and oiling, but it is also an activity that happens throughout the day. It may occur as a response to dirty or disarranged feathers or be a more routine activity, especially when the bird is resting. When waders preen without bathing they wet their bills beforehand.

Two preening techniques are used: nibbling with the bill opening and shutting, and stroking with the bill closed. The thoroughness of nibbling allows the bird to work oil into the plumages, to repair and rearrange plumage and remove extraneous material. The action involves the bird taking a feather or several feathers in its bill and passing them between the mandibles, moving upwards from the base

RIGHT *To scratch its bill the Black-winged Stilt stands on one leg and brings the other foot forward (top). This is called direct scratching. To scratch its head the stilt brings its foot over its wing (bottom). This is known as indirect scratching.*

of the feathers. It may also nibble around the base of the feather and the surrounding skin. Stroking is less painstaking and consists of drawing the closed bill across the plumage in the direction in which the the the feathers lie.

Preening seems to give comfort to birds and, when moulting, waders habitually preen before roosting.

SCRATCHING

Birds cannot use their bills to preen the feathers on their heads for obvious reasons. Instead they use their feet to preen the feathers by scratching. This usually takes place as part of the feather-care sequence. Like other animals they will also scratch their heads because of an itch and it is this spontaneous reaction that is the most frequent cause of scratching. When preening, the action is often slower and more deliberate than simple scratching.

To stretch the muscles and prepare the circulatory system for action, a Common Sandpiper stretches a wing and a leg.

To scratch its head, a bird must stand on one leg and raise the other to reach its head. There are two distinct methods of head-scratching: direct and indirect. In the first the foot is brought straight to the head, while in indirect scratching one wing is lowered and the foot on the same side is brought over the wing. Generally each species performs one or the other of these methods. Among the waders, plovers and Oystercatchers are indirect scratchers, Turnstones are direct scratchers and Black-winged Stilts and Avocets tend to scratch their heads indirectly and their bills directly.

SKIN CARE

Because waders live in wet, muddy places, their bills, legs and feet soon become dirty. In addition to maintaining their feathers, birds will pay attention to their feet and legs, picking off dirt, presumably when it irritates them. They will also remove extraneous matter at other times. Breeding waders wash their feet in water before returning to the nest and all waders will rinse their bills in water.

WING STRETCHING

Almost all birds perform single wing stretches. The function seems to be to stretch the muscles and prepare the circulatory system for action. The wing is extended sideways and lowered or raised until almost fully extended and then after a brief pause it is folded again. Sometimes the leg on the same side as the wing is stretched simultaneously. At other times just a leg may be stretched.

The other form of wing stretching involves both wings being lifted above the back. Waders stretch their wings upwards so that the tips almost touch. This is sometimes a signal to other members of the flock, both before take-off and immediately after landing.

SLEEPING AND RESTING

Although they often appear to be busy creatures, waders do not spend all their time in vigorous activity. Like all other warm-blooded animals they need to rest and to sleep. Resting, or loafing as it sometimes described, is a period during which activity, and consequently energy requirements, is kept to a minimum. It is also a reservoir of time, which can be used for foraging when food is scarce.

Birds sleep for approximately eight hours each day. Like human beings they spend a third of their time asleep, and, like human beings,

In spring, sleeping Lapwings share a neutral roosting ground, each male returning to defend his breeding territory at dawn and again in the evening.

individuals have different sleep requirements. There are also differences between species, seasons and geographical locations. In the short Arctic summers, breeding waders need to make use of the available daylight, but even when there is 24-hour midsummer daylight the birds are least active around midnight.

In most species roosting birds sleep communally outside the breeding season. Usually, this is on the shore or traditional salt-marsh sites, but Grey and Red-necked Phalaropes sleep on the water. During the breeding season most waders sleep at or near the nest. After they have paired, male and female Lapwings will roost in a neutral roosting ground, but the males will return to their territories at dawn and dusk to defend them.

No one is certain of the function of sleep in animals, but it is clearly important to the well-being of warm-blooded animals. Continued sleep deprivation increases the need for it and when it does come it is deeper and longer than normal, but lost sleep is not always made up with additional and equal time spent sleeping.

Sleep may have several function, and several theories have been put forward to define these, although none of them is entirely convincing. It has been suggested that sleep effectively shuts down the brain to allow it to process the information received during the waking day or that it is a device to save energy during a period when the effort involved would not justify the energy expended.

The brains of birds do seem to be active when they are sleeping, but no-one yet knows whether they are dreaming in a way recognizable to human beings. Sometimes birds' heads twitch slightly, but this is probably the effect of their muscles relaxing. A sleeping bird allows its head to droop or tucks it under its wings. Its breathing and heart-beat become slower and its body temperature falls slightly. Even in deep sleep the bird's eyes blink, an activity known as 'peeking'. A similar blinking can sometimes be seen in sleeping domestic dogs, but not every few minutes as happens with birds. The eye remains open for several seconds and may stay open longer when there is a disturbance. In deep sleep, peeking is less frequent than in shallow sleep or when the bird is a member of a flock.

Many birds have eyelids that are paler than the darker plumage around the eye. Thus, the eye is often more conspicuous when closed than when open. No-one is sure why this should be. The hypothesis that it makes the sleeping bird look as if it is awake is not convincing unless the eyes are also pale. In Avocets, for example, the eyes are dark and can barely be seen against the black head when they are open. Why, therefore, should a predator be fooled into thinking that the eye is open? And would it really deter a predator?

BREEDING

Like other birds, waders time their breeding season to coincide with the optimum conditions in which to lay eggs and rear young. Although by the time spring arrives some species may have already paired, it is then that courtship begins in earnest and territories are established, leading to copulation, egg-laying and rearing young.

TIMING

Birds in the south of the region breed earlier than those in the north. Resident populations and those that winter nearest to their breeding grounds also tend to breed early. Thus, the Stone Curlews of the Canary Islands, which do not migrate from the islands, begin to nest as early as February while those in mainland Europe, which have wintered in north Africa and southern Spain, lay in April.

Oystercatchers move from estuaries to their inland and coastal breeding grounds in February, but they may not breed for a further six weeks. The Curlews and Redshanks which share the Oyster-catchers' mud-flat feeding grounds move inland in March to the moorlands and wet-meadows where they breed. They begin to lay eggs in Britain in the first half of April. Professor Hale states that their return has become progressively earlier each year since the 1950s. More northerly populations in Scandinavia and Baltic countries breed later, possibly starting towards the end of May.

The waders that lay eggs in late March and April in temperate latitudes run the risk of losing eggs or chicks during very cold or very wet weather. Those that arrive later have no such problems. They have usually wintered further south. Common Sandpipers, which are often solitary migrants, begin their northward journey from sub-Saharan Africa to northern Europe in late March or April, avoiding the hazards of bad weather by starting to breed at the beginning of May.

The long-distance migrants that winter in Southern Africa and breed near or within the Arctic Circle complete a 20,000-km northward flight over several weeks, using the estuaries they had passed through in the autumn as staging posts. Once they arrive in their tundra breeding ground they have only a short time in which to breed. There may be no more than six or seven weeks between the spring thaw and the first autumn snowfall.

Sanderlings, which winter around the coasts of Africa as far south as the Cape, breed within the Western Palearctic at Spitsbergen and outside the region in Greenland, northern Canada and Arctic Russia. They are seen on their northward migration at the Camargue in April and May, on the Dutch coast and in Britain in May and in Finland in late May and early June. They arrive at their breeding areas in Russia and Spitsbergen in June and begin laying eggs in the middle of the month. If conditions are right, the breeding season will take little more than six weeks. Within eight or nine weeks, by the middle of August, the adults have left, to be followed by young birds in early September.

The short summer in the Arctic means that some waders may arrive when there is still snow cover, which makes feeding difficult. Bar-tailed Godwits guard against this by arriving in the tundra of Lapland and northern Russia with unused reserves of fat.

SEXUAL DIMORPHISM

With the exception of Ruffs, the differences between males and females among waders are not marked. Among waders, females tend to be larger than male, but in some species, such as the larger plovers and stilts, the males are larger. In the case of Ruffs the males are noticeable larger and bulkier than the females. Female Curlews tend to have longer bills than the males. The males usually have brighter plumage than their mates, but in species where females do most of the territorial display, such as Painted Snipes, Dotterels and phalaropes, they have the brighter plumage.

The tendency among waders is for the males to play the major role in rearing the young and, even where incubation is equally shared, it is often the male which stays with the young longer. The advantages of the males being smaller are not obvious, although it has been suggested that females prefer smaller males, because they are the most aerobatic display-fliers. Agility in flight may be a sign of physical fitness.

SITE FIDELITY

There are differences between species in their fidelity from year to year to breeding sites (also known as ortstreue or philopatry). Ringing studies have shown that Turnstones in Finland are faithful to their breeding sites. But information about waders breeding in the most northerly areas can be sparse, because the nest-sites are difficult for observers to reach. Limited ringing studies of Bar-tailed Godwits suggests that this species is faithful to feeding sites on migration and may, therefore, be faithful to breeding sites as well.

Golden Plovers show marked fidelity, not only to the area in which they hatched, but also to the same territory and even the same nest-site, with siblings nesting in neighbouring territories. Birds of either sex may return to the previous year's territory and take a new mate.

On the other hand, only some 70 per cent of Lapwings, which survive the winter return to within 20 km of the nest-site where they hatched. This means a comparatively wide distribution of indivi-duals and the spread of the 30 per cent which breed 20 km or more from their natal area has the effect of preventing sub-species from arising.

TERRITORY

In many groups of birds, the maintenance of breeding territories is a means of ensuring sufficient food for a growing family. Among the breeding waders of western Europe the purpose of maintaining breeding territories would appear to be more concerned with limiting populations and attempting to prevent 'unfaithfulness' than conserving food supplies in the breeding area. Because young waders are mobile, it is less important for them to conserve food than for passerines or raptors, whose young remain at the nest until they fledge.

By driving away other males, a territory-holder reduces the oppor-tunity of another male copulating with his mate. By doing this he is ensuring that her eggs are fertilized by him and that his genes are thereby passed on.

Among the most vigorus defenders of territory are the plovers and Lapwings. Perhaps the most familiar defence is the Lapwings' aerial display in which territory-holders fly parallel to the boundaries calling and tilting at rivals. From his arrival at the nesting area in March and April, the male rarely leaves the territory until the eggs are laid towards the end of April and early May, defending it against other males. Once the eggs have been laid the female joins in territorial defence particularly near the nest-site, but by this stage the defence is directed mainly against predators rather than other Lapwings.

Many pairs of Spur-winged Plovers in Israel remain in their breeding territories through the winter. Other Israeli-breeding plovers, and those that breed in Greece and Turkey, fly south in autumn and return in spring to territories selected by the males. They defend these vigorously until the territory is established, after which they appear to tolerate other birds. The display involves the territory-holder standing upright then running at the intruder, which usually takes flight almost immediately.

Ringed Plovers, which breed around the North Sea coasts and increasingly at inland sites such as gravel-pits, perform many of their

Lapwings display by flying parallel to the boundaries of their territories, tilting at rivals.

displays on the ground. They are highly territorial, but they often nest in loose groups. Nests may be as near as 5 m from each other or as far as 100 m apart. How the plovers behave within their territories varies between those areas where breeding and feeding grounds are adjacent and those where they are separate. Where the plovers feed and breed in adjacent areas they stay in their territories throughout the breeding season, but those that have to travel to feed spend most of their time in the feeding area rather than their territories when they are not incubating or tending young. The size of Ringed Plover territories varies from 250 m^2 to 850 m^2.

Both sexes perform threat displays in defence of territory until incubation begins and again when the young hatch. The display starts with the bird hunching its shoulders, fanning its tail and crouching with its body held horizontally to the ground. It runs at the intruder with its melodious threat call, which begins as three syllables, reduces to two and trails off with one. When near to the intruder, it stops with the feathers on the back raised, tail depressed and black chest patterns exaggerated. If the threat is more intense the bird may raise and fan its tail. This display may also form the beginning of the male's courtship of the female, whose response is appeasement shown by turning her head and body away.

If the intruder does not back away or appease the territory-holder, there might be a fight, in which the defender leaps in the air, kicking at the intruder. They will also fly at intruders. Ringed Plovers' aggression is so intense that birds of both sexes display vigorously at their own reflections in mirrors (introduced experimentally) and in the chrome hub-caps of cars parked on shingle beaches within their territories. Other species are not immune from attack. Although Ringed Plovers usually pick on birds of their own size, one was seen attacking a Shelduck, a bird many times larger.

Ringed Plovers are vigorous in their defence of breeding territories both against other plovers and birds of other species. This one is attacking a Shelduck which has wandered into its territory.

The closely related Kentish and Little Ringed Plovers are the most frequent victims of Ringed Plover attacks. The Little Ringed Plover, despite being smaller and less bulky, is more aggressive and may frequently initiate attacks on Ringed Plovers, which are almost always dominant because of their greater size.

The need for territories to ensure food supplies is not high in the short breeding season of the far north. Sandpipers hold terri-tories until after mating when they seem to lose their importance. Nevertheless while maintaining territories they may become very aggressive. Male Dunlins defending a territory will chase other species of waders as large as Greenshanks.

The role of territories among Dunlins appears to vary geog-raphically. In Alaska, Holmes showed a link between the size of territory and the availability of food. In an area where food supplies were plentiful and reliable he discovered 30 nests within an area of 40 ha; in a similarly sized area where food supplies were less reliable he found only six nests. By contrast, Soikkeli in Finland linked territory with sexual behaviour rather than with feeding. He found it difficult to estimate territory size, because the birds

moved through one another's territories on their journeys to and from their breeding grounds.

Different populations of the same species may show different nesting behaviour. The Redshanks in northern England are not territorial and nest semi-colonially, tolerating other Redshanks in feeding areas and in both the ground-space and air-space around their nests. It is not clear how territorial this species is in other areas, but there have been suggestions that in Germany they hold territories. Males are certainly aggressive towards each other when they first arrive at their breeding grounds, but this soon gives way to attempted courtship. The response of other males or unreceptive females is to move away.

ADVERTISING TERRITORY

Male birds holding territories advertise their possession in several ways. Calling and display-flights are common forms of advertising display. Unlike many of a bird's activities the intention is to draw attention to itself in relation to its territory, which means that it is comparatively easy to watch. In Oystercatchers it takes the form of a 'butterfly' flight in which the male flies with slow, deliberate, deep wing-beats which synchronize with each note of its steady 'kleew-kleew-kleew' flight call.

On the borders of their territories, Oystercatchers perform a 'piping' display against trespassers. This is a display employed in 80 per cent of neighbour disputes. Either sex will initiate the display. With head held forward and shoulders given a hunched appearance by the fluffed feathers on the neck and mantle, the bird points its slightly open bill towards the ground. Sometimes it vibrates its bill very rapidly. Usually it pipes as it displays, but it may perform silently. The piping bird will turn through a semi-circle or a complete circle and then run at the intruder, sometimes turning laterally towards it. The mate often joins in and the anxiety may be so infectious that birds from nearby territories may join in the display. Piping parties of up to five birds are not uncommon, but up to 30 have been recorded. Two or more will run up and down together. Larger groups may run in line abreast for 25–30 m before suddenly turning and running again. Sometimes the group may face in a circle and pipe in unison.

Piping displays are usually over within a couple of minutes, but they may last up to five and have continued for a quarter of an hour. The length of these displays appears to be linked to the number of participants: the more birds that take part, the longer the display lasts. Sometimes the pipers take to the air, flying in a posture that

The hunched shoulders and downward-pointing bill are characteristic of the Oystercatcher's piping display against trespassers. Both members of a pair will take part and may be joined by neighbours.

mirrors their piping stance with the same hunched shoulders and the bill pointing downwards.

Another unusual territorial display flight is that of the Snipe. Males use a 'song-flight' to establish their ownership of a territory, but the 'song' has more in common with that of some insects than with other birds, because it is created mechanically rather than vocally. Although it is not uncommon to hear the air vibrating the wing feathers of birds as they fly, the drumming of Snipes is created through vibration of the outer tail feathers. The male takes off, rising at an angle of 10 per cent, flies in a wide circle for between 80 m and 120 m, before changing to a switchback flight, increasing the angle of flight to 30 per cent until it reaches 50 m. Then, it tilts into a 45 per cent dive with wings still beating and tail fanned so that the outermost tail feather on each side stands proud. The drumming sound is caused by the air vibrating the outer tail feathers during the dive, which lasts for up to two seconds before the bird goes into a glide before regaining height and repeating the performance. It follows a

As the air vibrates the outermost tail feathers of the Snipe it creates a drumming sound. The Snipe uses this unmistakable sound to proclaim its territory.

more or less circular course 150–200 m in diameter with the climbs going inwards and the dives outwards. The longest continuous drumming displays last more than one hour.

On moorlands, male Golden Plovers can be very aggressive in defence of territory, disputing hummocks or boulders from which to proclaim proprietorship. The males with the darker breasts are more likely to be aggressive and to copulate with females from neighbouring territories. Males perform display-flights as part of both courtship and territorial advertisement. They fly at about 20 m above the ground and more or less follow the territorial boundary. The flight is slow and buoyant with a slow, high upstroke and with a downstroke that goes below the horizontal. It is accompanied by a wailing call.

The familiar bubbling call of the Curlew, so beloved of radio drama producers who wish to create a moorland atmosphere, often accompanies this species' display-flight along the borders of its territory. Sometimes the call may be a low whistling.

Colonial nesters, such as Avocets, have less need of territorial displays. They may defend a small area around the nest. The size of this area seems to be variable, with a radius of up to 3 m in Suffolk, but twice that radius in Hungary. This variation is probably the result of the numbers of breeding birds and the comparative productivity of the habitats. Solitarily nesting Avocets defend larger areas. Because they are such strikingly patterned creatures they have little need to display to advertise their territories. Before the eggs hatch, pairs of Avocets will defend one or more feeding territories and after the young have hatched they maintain brood territories from which other birds are excluded. By the time the young are three weeks old they are very mobile. Some adults may no longer defend the territory, but others may continue until after the young have fledged. As all the birds at Avocet colonies do not breed at the same time, the same territories may be used by more than one pair in a season.

COURTSHIP DISPLAYS

Among waders there is a proportional bias in favour of males. In selecting a mate there is a consequent competition which takes two forms: intrasexual and intersexual. Intrasexual selection involves birds of one sex choosing a mate, while intersexual selection has been described by Birkhead and Moller as a 'contest between the salesmanship of one sex and the sales resistance by the other'.

Where the female makes the choice, as is the case with communally displaying species such as Ruffs and Great Snipes, there are two theories. In the first, the choice is arbitrary with females being attracted by the males' secondary sexual characteristics, such as the Ruff's ruffs, which offer no immediate or obvious benefits. Field observations do suggest that the development of the males' plumage is one of the criteria by which the females make their choice.

In the second theory, the purpose of the female's choices is to mate with a particular male because his secondary sexual characteristics reveal information about him. These characteristics may denote phenotypic quality (the physical constitution determined by the interaction between genetic make-up and environment), or resistance to parasites and disease, or other traits that indicate that this particular bird has a propensity for survival.

When they arrive back at their breeding grounds some waders have already paired. The bond in most Oystercatchers persists from year to year with one pair's record of up to 20 years in one territory. Some winter together while others spend the winter apart and meet again in pre-breeding flocks.

Among some species of waders, the sexes arrive at different times. From colour-ringing studies, it seems that male Greenshanks arrive before the females. Female Red-necked Phalaropes, on the other hand, arrive back first at their breeding grounds in Shetland and northern Scandinavia. Similarly, female Dotterels are the first to reach their breeding areas in the tundra around the Yenisey delta in northern Russia and the males arrive about ten days later. But the Scottish Dotterels arrive back in small mixed flocks, small single-sex flocks, as individuals or as pairs.

Both sexes of Dunlins return to their Arctic breeding grounds at the same time. They do not usually pair before arrival, but when their arrival is delayed by snow they will be paired by the time they reach the breeding grounds.

Dunlins show great faithfulness to their breeding areas. First-year birds return to the area where they hatched and half of them nest within 20 m of the nest where they hatched. Males are more faithful to nest-sites than females, but of those that remained as pairs for more than one season three-quarters nested within 100 m of their last nest-site and the remainder within 300 m.

In the Arctic, waders have only a short period for courtship before laying eggs and rearing young. In more temperate zones, there is no food shortage and less urgency to complete their breeding cycle before the return of winter and courtship may take place over several months.

At first, the ceremonies may be piecemeal. The song-flights, which delineate territories and warn other males to keep away, are also intended to attract mates. In these flights, the wing-beats are slower than normal and the wings quiver. The positions in which the wings are held vary between species. Greenshanks and Redshanks hold theirs in an arc below the horizontal while Knots and Curlews hold theirs in a 'V'-shape above the horizontal. Wing-quivering may be alternated with glides and this combination may develop into a switchback display flight. As the flight ends the displaying bird raises its wings and glides to the ground. As the season progresses this display-flight may develop into full courtship display.

One of the two main courtship displays of Redshanks is performed mainly by unpaired males while the other is performed by males which have already paired.

The main courtship display of paired Redshanks is ground-chasing. When it starts in late winter the chase appears to be random, promiscuous and, since it does not lead to copulation, unsuccessful. However, it reaches its greatest intensity in April and May when display-flights are over and pairs established. The chases are usually over in one or two minutes and often finish in copulation.

The Greenshank keeps its wings in an arc below the horizontal when it is performing a display-flight and the Curlew holds its wings above the horizontal.

Both pursuer and pursued tilt their bodies forward. The pursuer fluffs his feathers, fans his tail and lowers his head. The female holds her wings away from her body, with tail partly fanned and often stretching her head forward. To keep her in sight the male either runs sideways of cocks his head at an angle of about 20 per cent. The birds keep a 2-m space between them. If the gap shortens, the pursued flutters to increase the distance and, if it lengthens, the pursuer flutters to catch up.

The unmated Redshanks perform display-flights with the aim of attracting a mate. Despite this purpose, other males including those that are already paired do not molest the displaying male. They do not seem to claim air-exclusion zones around their nests and a display-flight for 1 km across the breeding ground of 100 pairs produces no reaction from the males.

The flight begins with a steep climb to at least 40 m at the top of which the bird changes to the switchback flight of downward glides on depressed wings succeeded by rising on rapidly quivering wings still kept below the horizontal. The head is held up and the tail fanned. Each undulation lasts for 2–12 seconds. Throughout the flight the bird delivers a harsh, squealing 'tyee' song. When the flight is successful, a female is attracted into the air and follows him until he alights either at the proposed nest-site or in his feeding area.

The frequency of these flights reaches a peak by the end of March or the beginning of April when they diminish as pairs form. A second peak occurs when young, unmated Redshanks arrive towards the end of April. The longest flights, of up to four minutes, have been recorded in May. Most take place around noon, but not when the winds are high. Throughout the flight the male has a regular, rapid and insistent song, a loud, clear 'tyoo', which may change on alighting to an excited yodel in which the female joins. When the male flies in to land at the end of the display, he holds his wings below the horizontal and changes his song to a musical yodel. As the female follows him he may perform an alighting ceremony in which he stands with wings uplifted and sings for about three minutes. A similar display may be performed when a mated bird alights near its sitting mate and may culminate in copulation.

While male Redshanks perform a display-flight aimed at attracting a mate into the air, the purpose of the Woodcock's display-flight, known as 'roding', is to attract the attention of a female which will call him down to the ground. There is an element of territorial proclamation about roding, but the roding grounds of more than one male may overlap. These flights take place at dawn and dusk throughout the breeding season as the male flies along woodland rides or above the tree-tops. The wing-beats are slower than in normal flight and the breadth of the Woodcock's wings give the flight an owl-like quality. The birds may give a trisyllabic call when roding.

The Snipe's drumming flight (*see* page 97) is used for sexual display as well as to advertise a territory. Both sexes of Oystercatchers perform a whirring display-flight with rapid wing-beats.

Few human eyes are skilled enough to sex adult Avocets in the field, but some females do have an area of pale feathers around the base of the bill and the faint suggestion of a pale eye-ring. It is thought that there may be some subtle differences in the shapes of bills and in voice, and Avocets seem to have no difficulty in telling a he from a she. However, the mating ceremony may reinforce sexual differences for those birds that are not quite sure.

There is a ghostlike quality to the roding flight of the male Woodcock. Flying at tree-top height at dawn and dusk the Woodcock performs this flight to proclaim his territory and to attract the attention of a female on the ground.

The initial stages of the mating ceremonies may be seen when Avocets first return to their western European breeding grounds in March. Courtship on the RSPB nature reserves at Minsmere Levels and Havergate Island in Suffolk is an early morning activity, taking place between 6 a.m. and 10 a.m., which makes it difficult for visitors to see, because the boat to Havergate does not leave until 10 a.m., and Minsmere only opens to visitors at 9 a.m. This emphasizes the lack of synchronicity between the activities of birds and the leisure habits of human beings.

The mating ceremony may be initiated when the male and female are loafing or preening together or when one of the pair approaches the other when 'scything' for food. One of the pair will start to preen and repeatedly dip its bill in the water, starting a dip-shake-preen display. The preening is nibble-preening, concentrated on the upper breast. At any time, but particularly early in the season, the display may stop there. However, it continues if the female adopts a soliciting posture with her head lowered. The male moves behind her from side to side three to five times, but sometimes more, dipping and shaking his bill and then preening. Moving beside the female, he dips his bill near her legs with a splash, shakes his bill and preens his breast. There the sequence may end, if the female raises her head and starts to feed or preen, or if the male turns away from instead of towards her.

If the sequence continues, the displaying male walks round and behind the female in decreasing semi-circles until he approaches so closely that he must stoop to clear her tail. He moves beside her again, increasing the tempo of his bill-dipping until it is continuously submersed in water. Suddenly he mounts his mate with wings uplifted. In response to the female's swinging her head from side to side, he bends his legs and positions himself for copulation, which follows with customary avian rapidity. The birds cross their bills briefly, then run side by side with the male's wings still lowered and with one over his mate's back. They then walk or run in hunched postures.

Closely related to Avocets, Black-winged Stilts have four similar displays: butterfly-flight; high-leaping display in which the bird drops with spread wings; grouping ceremony, which usually occurs before nesting and in which three or four birds congregate calling with a

The sequence of Avocets' mating ceremony starts with a dip-shake-preen display by the male. The female adopts a submissive posture and the male walks around her in ever-decreasing circles, dipping his bill until it is submerged. He mounts her with wings uplifted. Copulation follows in response to her swinging her head from side to side. After copulation they run side by side.

loud crooning note, attracting other birds and flying at at a height of up to 5 m and hang with legs dangling for about 30 seconds; and a mating ceremony, similar to the Avocets', which lasts about a minute. During mating, the female holds her soliciting posture throughout the ceremony and this posture is so strong a stimulus to males that they have been seen to try to mate with inanimate objects which happen to have a similar position.

Although casual copulation between one partner of an established pair and a third bird is not uncommon, most species of waders stay with one partner for at least a season. Painted Snipes are exceptions to this. Not only is there role-reversal with females performing a remarkable courtship display, but the females have as many as four mates.

When the female displays, she stands laterally to the male with one wing raised and spread, the other may be either folded or spread downwards, and the tail is spread. As the display becomes more intense she turns to face the male and brings forward both wings until the carpal joints are in line with her head. Her feathers are fluffed, her tail is spread and her bill is pointed towards the ground. She may sway backwards and forwards, with a mellow advertising call reminiscent of the sound made by blowing across the top of a bottle. The display lasts for a couple of minutes and is followed by copulation, after which the birds stand beside each other.

Most female Painted Snipes mate with at least two males and some may do so with three or four. Each female lays at least two clutches and her bond with the male lasts for as long as it takes to complete a four-egg clutch (probably four or five days). Once the clutch is laid she moves on leaving the male to incubate the eggs. Over the following twelve days she woos and wins another mate and lays her next clutch, again taking no part in their incubation.

Perhaps the best-known of the waders in which males have more than one mate are Ruffs. The males perform communal displays in which they vie for the favours of the females. For most of the year males and females lead separate lives coming together only to mate. Outside the breeding season the flocks are usually sexually segregrated even when both sexes are present at the same roosting or feeding grounds.

In spring, it is the females which are first to arrive at the breeding areas. Once they have returned in spring or early summer the males congregate at the display-grounds, known as 'arenas' or 'leks'. Some areas are traditional, recorded as being in use 100 years ago, but the Dutch authority on Ruffs, Johan Van Rhijn, instances many arenas of recent origin. Arenas tend to be in clusters and may

At the communal display grounds of Ruffs females select mates from the dominant males with well-grown ruffs and head-tufts. The satellite males tend to have white ruffs or head-tufts.

be within 100 m of each other. Each covers about 20 m² and tends
to be near water on slightly raised ground.

Each 'resident' male has a territory or 'court' of about 1 m in
diameter which is 1 m or 1.5 m from the next. In the centre of each
court there are small patches which rapidly become bare of soil.
Dominant males occupy courts in the middle of the arena. Younger
birds tend to occupy those on the margins, progressing towards the
centre in subsequent years. Beyond the margins are satellite males,
which do not usually fight or even threaten others, but which may
take the opportunity of copulating with a female when a dominant
male's back is turned.

There are so many combinations of plumage among male Ruffs
that it is very unusual to find two identical birds. However, Van Rhijn
has shown a relationship between the combinations of plumage colours
and the status of the individuals. The court-holding or independent
males in central Europe and Scandinavia have predominantly dark
ruffs and head-tufts while satellites tend to have white ruffs and
head-tufts: coloured ruffs and black head-tufts occur in more than
half the dominant males and among the satellites half have white
ruffs or white head-tufts or both. The plumage type is usually
consistent from year to year and individuals' status seems to be
determined in the second season.

The independents tolerate the satellites because they attract the
females initially. It is possible that satellites mate on migration.
In addition to the plumage differences it seems that there are
morphological differences between independents and satellites, with
the former having longer wings and being heavier.

The satellites rarely behave aggressively and when an independent
male adopts a threatening, squatting posture the satellite will squat
submissively and, if the dominant male spreads his tail and moves
his body forward, the satellite flees. The function of the satellites
appears to attract the females to the lek, but once this has been done
their role is finished, unless they can sneak an opportunist copulation.
The dominant males least tolerant of satellites are those that have the
most copulations.

Females seem to show attachment neither to particular leks or to
particular plumage patterns. Development of plumage in the males
and their holding central positions in the arena seem to be the main
attractions to females. These are older males and they perform the
greatest number of successful copulations.

The Ruff's lek is not, however, a continuous scene of activity. Much
of the time, the atmosphere is relaxed with the rival males preening
or resting. Males then begin to spar, intruding on each other's courts,
seeing off satellites and greeting approaching females with a wing-
fluttering greeting ceremony. If the male is too enthusiastically

aggressive to other males, females may be deterred. It seems that it is the older males which have the experience to enable them to temper their aggression and not to deter the females.

Dominant males copulate most frequently and one of the nine males at a Dutch lek achieved over half of the 100 copulations seen over the season. The lekking season continues for six to eight weeks from the second half of April in the Netherlands, from early May in Germany and from mid-May in Norway. Each day, the males begin to arrive before dawn and stay for all or most of the daylight hours. Females arrive after dawn.

Copulation may follow quickly for some females, but others may be present for hours without copulating. Males may mate with several successive females and, although females seldom stay for more than a few hours, they may mate with more than one male. Opportunities for mating between females and marginal or satellite males do occur away from the lek and may occur on migration.

Another lekking species is the Great Snipe. Its displays start in May within a few days of the birds returning to their northern breeding grounds and continue until the end of June. Sometimes, more than one area is visited by individual males. Lacking the dramatic courtship adornments of the Ruffs, male Great Snipes draw attention to themselves by performing extravagant movements in which they stretch their necks so far back that they are almost touching their backs and by simultaneously rattling their bills to make continuous clicking noises, another contrast with silent display of Ruffs. The leks begin around twilight and continue into the night. Females arrive several hours after the males.

Communal displays may have several advantages to the species that perform them. By displaying in groups the males may be safer from predators because of the principal of safety in numbers in flocks. The marginal and satellite males to raise the alarm when the other males are too absorbed in their courtship to notice approaching danger. The activity of the flock will also attract females. Since the lek lasts for several weeks, there are opportunities for late arrivals and females which come late into breeding condition to copulate.

COPULATION

The act of copulation in waders is, as is the case with most birds, perfunctory. It requires an excellent balancing ability, as the male must perch on the back of the female and twist his rump to bring his cloaca into contact with the female's. The female with the male on her back has to twist her rump in the opposite direction. The contact

Lacking the adornments of Ruffs, male Great Snipes at the lek rely on extravagant movements and calling to attract mates.

is brief and the male dismounts after a few seconds. In many cases, copulation is the culmination of a courtship ceremony, but sometimes birds will copulate without warning.

Before copulation, male Greenshanks and Redshanks approach the females with wings held vertically. Woodcocks copulate either when they land after roding or after a display on the ground with tail fanned, tail raised and wings drooping.

PAIR-BONDS

The brevity of the pair-bond of Temminck's Stints is almost as short as that of species which display communally. Both sexes are bigamous in succession in a manner reminiscent of Arthur Snitzler's play *La Ronde*, in which each character had an affair with another, who had an affair with another until the last affair involves the first character.

*Greenshanks copulate, the male balancing precariously on the back
of the female.*

The love-life of the Temminck's Stint is not quite so neat, but it
does show greater sexual equality. A female mates with a male, which
incubates the clutch she lays. The pair-bond lasts no more than a
week by which time the clutch is complete. She then mates with a
second male. This time she incubates the resulting clutch.

Meanwhile during breaks from his incubation duties the first male
mates with a second female, who this time incubates her own clutch.
Thus, by the males being polygynous and the female being polyandrous,
the production of eggs is doubled. In the short Arctic summer, there is
no time for a single female to lay and rear a second successive brood,
but the Temminck's Stint's strategy increases the production of young
in one summer. Sometimes the pattern goes wrong: the ambition of
the males exceeds their abilities and they will mate with more than
two females, which results in a clutch being laid with no bird to
incubate. This provides a lucky bonus to an Arctic Fox or Raven.

Other species have pair-bonds that last longer than those of either
Ruffs or Temminck's Stints, but this does not mean total 'faithfulness'.

Given the opportunity, either member of an established pair may stray. Although generally monogamous, male Oystercatchers will copulate promiscuously, attempting copulation with several females, sometimes successfully. Established pairs may copulate without warning. The calling male may approach a female when she is feeding. If she stops feeding and tilts forward slightly, he will mount with no preliminary ceremony.

If a female is left unattended at certain times, she may be approached by, and accept the attentions of, a passing male. To prevent this, a male Oystercatcher closely guards his mate during egg-laying, when he has a vested interest in ensuring that it is his sperm which fertilize his mate's eggs. In addition to keeping away unwanted rivals, this protects the female and eggs from predators.

Redshanks stay together from year to year. Pairs have been recorded as staying together for seven breeding seasons. They maintain their bond by displaying. They trill, glide on curved wings, land and hold their wings for a few seconds, both trilling. Common

Common Sandpipers perform display flights as part of pair-bonding, flying with shallow wing beats and gliding on down-curved wings.

Sandpipers perform a similar bonding display, as do Curlews, but their wings are held up as they glide.

Most Golden Plovers mate for life, but promiscuity is not uncommon. Some pairs appear to be incompatible or the attraction of another individual is so strong that one of the pair deserts its mate.

While studying plovers in Kincardineshire, R.G. Parr noted three cases of polyandrous females. In the first, two days after the young had hatched, the female moved to a new territory and a new mate, laying a second clutch of eggs. Her first mate reared the young of the first clutch. The next year she remained with the second mate. In the second case another female deserted her mate and mated in the following year with the deserted male from the first case. In the third case the female deserted four days after the young had hatched and was seen with another male over 1 km away. No nest was found and the following year she returned to her original mate and bred successfully.

The pair-bond is particularly important in species that nest colonially. Gregarious living provides Avocets and stilts with countless opportunities to copulate outside the pair. Pairs arrive already paired, but there is no evidence that the pair-bond is maintained throughout the winter.

NESTS

Waders are not nest-makers in the same class as perching birds. Most species content themselves with scrapes in the soil or pebbles on a beach. Creating a nest-scrape takes minutes rather than days and waders can afford to make several. Nest-scraping often forms an important element of display. Male Ringed Plovers, and males of the closely related Kentish and Little Ringed Plovers, will crouch to push their breasts into the ground, rotating and kicking the soil and vegetation away. Having made the first depression, the male calls to the female while fanning, raising and lowering his tail. She enters the scrape and rotates, vigorously kicking out soil and vegetation.

On the Orkney island of North Ronaldsay, some Ringed Plovers nest under cover, using sites beneath boulders and walls. Seven of eighteen nests found by M.G. Pennington in 1987 were covered and these had a higher success rate, possibly because they escaped interference from sheep and were less exposed to the high winds which blow across the island.

While the plovers usually choose open sites, which makes it relatively easy to watch their displays, many sandpipers and 'shanks do so amid ground plants, which makes observation their scrape-displays more difficult. The male Redshank makes up to fifteen scrapes, and the female will select the one in which she wishes to lay her eggs. One of the unused nests may be used by the male as a roosting place while his mate incubates. The female lines the selected nest with plant material.

Some waders follow the practice, more usually associated with raptors, of using other birds' deserted nests. Green Sandpipers use the nests of thrushes and Wood Pigeons, Red Squirrel dreys or natural platforms of twigs, such as the witches' broom. Sometimes they nest on tussocks on the ground. The closely related Wood Sandpipers usually nest on the ground, but will occasionally use the nests of Redwings, which tend to be built near the ground.

Beach-nesting waders often line their scrapes with shells. Ringed Plovers use shells to camouflage their nests. Oystercatchers, some of which may lay in bare scrapes, may collect large numbers of shells with which to ring the edge of the nest. However, when Oystercatchers nest on grass or salt-marsh this habit, which may provide an element of camouflage on a beach, only serves to draw attention to the nest.

The amount of plant material used by sandpipers in nests depends on availability and the likelihood of flooding. In flood meadows, they will nest on hummocks to which they add nesting material to raise the nest above flood-level. When floods threaten their nests, Black-winged Stilts will add plant material to stay above water-level.

Stilts nest in loose colonies of up to 100 pairs, but normally colonies have 10–40 pairs. They often associate with breeding Avocets, Slender-billed Gulls, lake terns, Lapwings, Redshanks and Collared Pratincoles. Although tolerant of the other species, they are territorial towards each other and will rise in a 'dread' as a mass defence against Marsh Harriers.

EGGS

Egg-laying usually begins four to six days after the spring temperatures rise. Red-necked Phalaropes begin to lay three or four days after the temperature reaches 8 °C. The first egg in most wader species is laid within two days of copulation. While the females are producing eggs they increase their intake of calcium and will eat bones and other calcitic material.

Eggs from which well-developed young hatch need to be as large as possible. However, they are distinctly pointed, so that when arranged with the points facing inwards they fit snugly together and take up the minimum space.

Apart from the eggs of Crab Plovers which are laid in holes in sandy ground and have no need for protective colouring, the eggs of

Most waders nest on or very near the ground, but the Green Sandpiper will take over nests in trees deserted by other birds.

waders are cryptically coloured. The ground colour of the eggs varies from cream to dark brown and all are spotted or blotched with shades of grey, olive, brown and black. Such patterns allow the eggs to blend with their surroundings. The sand plovers and ringed plovers, which nest on open beaches, lay eggs which merge with the surrounding sand and gravel. The eggs of Ringed Plovers, for example, have a sandy background colour with small dark blotches, which, although they may be quite sparsely distributed, are enough to break up the regular outline of the egg. Stone Curlews' eggs, which are longer and less pointed than other waders' eggs, are comparatively well-blotched which allows them to merge with the pebbles and stones on their heathland nest-sites.

The effects of local light and shade are mimicked in some species' eggs. Redshanks, breeding in damp meadows among grasses, lay eggs with dark blotches which mirror the shadows thrown by the vegetation around the nest. Snipes, which nest in wetter areas than Redshanks, lay eggs whose blotches are patchier, reflecting the areas of light and shade on pools of water. In the chiaroscuro of the woodland floor, the pale blotched eggs of Woodcocks disappear from view. Some waders add to the protection of their eggs by using plants and sand to cover their eggs when they leave them.

Most waders lay four eggs, which appears to be the optimal number for tending nidifugous young on land. There is a tendency for those species nesting nearer to the equator to lay smaller clutches – these are also often species which feed their young in the early stages: Stone Curlews lay clutches of one to three eggs; Collared Pratincoles lay three eggs; and Crab Plovers, whose young remain in the nest-hole for some days after hatching, lay one egg.

If the first clutch has been destroyed most species will lay a second clutch. Redshanks may lay two replacement clutches. Some species are double-brooded. Stone Curlews and Woodcocks are usually single-brooded, but each species may lay a second clutch. The double-brooded Ringed Plovers may even manage a third brood. Similarly, Spur-winged Plovers in Israel rear two broods and may sometimes rear a third.

Some of the tundra-nesting species have the strategy of simult-aneous double-brooding, in which two clutches are laid and each parent looks after one. In this way Sanderlings and Temminck's Stints manage to rear up to eight young in the short, eight-week season. Sanderlings share the work with the male taking one clutch and the female the other, while Temminck's Stints have a more complex partner-swapping system (*see* page 111).

The complete clutch of waders' eggs is usually between half and three-quarters of the weight of the female. Among stints it is even greater with the clutch weight of 90 per cent of the female's weight. This means that for females of the almost simultaneously double-brooded Temminck's Stints' egg-laying means producing up to 180 per cent of their weight within ten to twelve days. Some may even lay a third clutch, which, even if not completed, would mean that they would lay more than twice their weight in eggs.

There is an interval, between the laying of each egg, which is between 30 and 36 hours in most species, but tends to be shorter in the more northerly nesting species. In Sanderlings, for example, the laying interval is between 26 and 29 hours. If the weather becomes colder during this period, laying intervals may lengthen. The first eggs are often lost to predators and the female may move to another scrape and lay either a smaller clutch or a complete clutch. If the full clutch is lost, the bird may start a replacement clutch within a few days or wait for up to a fortnight. A four-egg clutch takes five or six days to complete.

During the period when the female Oystercatcher is laying, her mate stands guard against opportunistic males and predators. When she leaves the nest to feed he accompanies her, leaving the eggs at risk from predators. The farther the birds are nesting from the feeding areas, the greater the risk to the eggs. That the male accompanies the female and leaves the eggs suggests that it is more important to protect any unlaid eggs from fertilization by a passing opportunist than to protect the eggs already laid from predators.

INCUBATION

When the final egg is laid incubation begins. This maintains the eggs at a constant temperature of between 34 per cent and 39 per cent needed for the embryo to develop within the egg. Because of physiological changes to incubating birds during breeding they are able to keep these temperatures relatively constant. The feathers are moulted from the lower breast to reveal a brood-patch, in which the blood-vessels are close to the surface of the skin. The feathers surrounding the brood-patch are fluffed to expose it and allow the heat to be transferred when the body of the incubating bird comes into contact with the eggs.

In temperate latitudes the air temperature rarely reaches 34 °C, but in the south of the region where air temperatures may be higher birds have to adopt strategies to keep the eggs cool. Therefore, in some cases, the incubation takes the form of shading with the body. Egyptian Plovers crouch above the eggs to cast shade on them, but they may also bury their eggs or regurgitate water over them to keep them cool. However, when it becomes cool at night they need to incubate to keep the temperature of eggs up. Sand-grouse-like behaviour is sometimes adopted by Spur-winged Plovers, which will sometimes moisten their feathers with water before returning to their nests. Shared incubation happens in many species, but the share is not usually equal, the female taking the greater part. Shared incubation allows the eggs to be incubated for up to 90 per cent of each 24 hours, but when a single bird incubates less time is spent on the nest.

In Sanderlings, males and females each incubate a separate clutch for 75 per cent of the day. Temminck's Stints incubate for a similar percentage of the time, taking a five-or ten-minute break every ten to 25 minutes. The length of these periods varies between individuals and are longer at night, in cold weather or when it rains.

Males of the communally displaying Ruffs and Great Snipes take no share in the incubation. Conversely among phalaropes and Dotterels, it is the males alone which incubate.

The length of incubation is usually about three weeks, but is shorter in many of the species breeding further north and it tends to be longer in larger species. Thus, Red-necked Phalaropes take 17 days and Curlews 30.

Losses of eggs during incubation vary, but all ground-nesters are vulnerable to predation by rats, foxes, hedgehogs and sheep among others, to trampling by cattle and careless, or unknowing human beings, and to flooding, particularly on the seashore and salt-marshes. Ringed Plovers may lose up to 15 per cent of their eggs through such loss or infertility, which Hale calculates as a success rate of 3.23–3.35 eggs per nest. Losses to Redshanks on salt-marshes are much higher and may be as high as 75 per cent due to trampling by cattle and flooding.

GROWTH OF YOUNG

Because incubation begins after the last egg has been laid, all four eggs in the clutch hatch within 24 hours of each other. Young waders emerge from the egg covered in down, mobile and in most cases able to find their own food. The chick chips its way out using its

A pair of Stone Curlews swap incubation duties, revealing three well-camouflaged oval eggs.

egg-tooth, a horny projection on its upper mandible, which falls off within a couple of days of hatching. When the chick emerges from the egg its feathers are damp, but they soon dry and within 24 hours most chicks have left the nest. Young Oystercatchers, however, remain in the nest for two or three days and their parents bring them food.

Although they are able to walk and feed themselves, young waders stay in family groups accompanied by one or both parents, who protect them from predators and keep them warm. For about fourteen days after hatching one or both of the parents brood their young to keep them warm and dry in rainy weather. As the young develop contour feathers they are able to control their own body heat and their parents spend less time brooding them.

Like waders' eggs, their vulnerable young are coloured to merge with their surroundings. The colours are predominantly browns and greys with dark brown streaks and patches. The patterns reflect both the habitat in which they breed and their eventual adult plumage. Thus, Little Ringed Plovers chicks have sandy-coloured heads and backs with fine dark blotches, which provide cryptic colouring against river gravels, while the white breast and nape are a promise of the adult plumage to come. Broad-billed Sandpipers, which nest among the mosses and prostrate flowers of the tundra, have chicks with dark-blotched, cryptic plumage. The young of grassland-breeders, such as Redshanks, have striped back patterns which mimic the surrounding vegetation. The chicks of both Grey and Golden Plovers are golden with the young Grey Plovers possibly more so than the Golden Plovers.

For a day or two after hatching, the chicks lose a little weight but then they begin to gain it rapidly. In the first five days, phalaropes almost treble their weight and Dunlins double theirs. The larger Snipes take seven days to double their weight. Because they have yet to develop their long bills, chicks are unable to find food beneath the surface and are, therefore, dependent on the local hatch of insects which they take from plants and the ground.

By the time they fledge, young waders have not reached their adult weight and, despite the fact that their primaries are still growing, they can fly. Red-necked Phalaropes, which have a short breeding cycle, can fly within eighteen to twenty days of hatching. The larger Curlews and Oystercatchers take up to 42 days. For most waders the first primaries last for fifteen months until the autumn moult of the following year (for moult sequence see pages 73–8).

In some species, both parents stay with their young until fledging and beyond, but in others one parent, often the female, will leave parental care to the other. Female Dunlins, for example, leave their broods with the male a few days after hatching. In the Arctic, this also happens with other species. When the need to brood is lessened at about fourteen days, the male Curlew Sandpipers, female Dotterels and female phalaropes move south, leaving the care of the young to their mates. The removal of half the adults may be a strategy to ensure that there is sufficient food for the young.

As we have seen, young and adults in some populations migrate separately, but in other species the family stays together. Families of Lapwings move together from their breeding grounds joining up with other families to form wintering flocks.

DEFENCE OF NESTS AND YOUNG

Nesting waders face two types of enemy: the predatory and the clumsy. The first category includes ground predators, such a foxes, mustelids, rats, snakes, and other birds, such as larger gulls, corvids, Kestrels, Marsh Harriers and other raptors. The second category are those animals that accidentally damage eggs and young. They are usually large, bumbling creatures like grazing cattle and human beings.

A sitting Ringed Plover can be remarkably difficult to see against the pebbles of a beach.

The most obvious defence against predators is cryptic colouring, or camouflage, which can be a disadvantage for ground-nesters because it hides them from the view of the clumsy. A cryptically coloured creature which freezes is much less likely to be discovered than one which runs. For young waders, still unable to fly, running for safety is the wrong thing to do. Firstly they would be outrun by most predators and, even if they were not caught, they would become separated from the rest of the family.

With a few exceptions, adult waders are cryptically coloured, which is particularly important when incubating or brooding young. They, too, freeze when danger approaches and hope to pass unnoticed by the predator. Both Woodcocks and Jack Snipes are cryptically patterned, the first blotched for leafier, woodland floors and the second streaked for wet, grassy places. Each is strongly attached to sitting tight and, even outside the breeding season, will freeze, only flying if a person approaches within a few metres.

In its reddish breeding plumage, the Knot looks much more splendid than in its more subtle grey winter plumage. Against a background of greyish estuarine mud the Knots, still in breeding plumage, stand out like sore thumbs. However, against the patchy browns, reds and greens of their tundra breeding grounds the

birds disappear. Profiled on a page of a field guide the Ringed Plovers with their striking black-and-white breast and face markings look conspicuous, but this is not always so in the field. Ringed Plovers incubating on a nest on a pebble beach on a bright day can be remarkably difficult to see, because the markings disrupt the outlines of the birds.

Sometimes a predator approaches to a point where the sitting bird can no longer bear to sit still. It will try to slip from the nest unnoticed. When it is a few metres from the nest the plover may drop one wing and flop away from the nest as if it were injured. The predator, attracted by the prospect of an injured and therefore easy-to-kill adult bird, will follow it away from the nest. Once at a safe distance the bird will take off. Although injury-feigning is common among plovers and lapwings, not every individual will perform such displays. Other waders perform slightly different distraction displays. Dunlins, Purple Sandpipers, Knots, Curlews and

To lead a predator away from its nest a Little Ringed Plover feigns injury to its wing.

A Woodcock carries a chick to safety by holding between her thighs.

Ruffs jump into the air as if trying unsuccessfully to fly. A Black-winged Stilt whose nest is threatened may employ a number of strategies including moving away from the nest and pecking at the ground or preening as if it were busy doing anything other than incubating eggs.

One defensive technique, is the way in which Woodcocks are alleged to carry young out of danger by holding them between their legs as they fly. Ornithologists who doubted the veracity of such observations put forward imaginative rationalizations, but there have been enough well-documented accounts of Woodcocks and other waders doing this for it to now be accepted as a fact. They have also been seen to carry chicks in their bills. Common Sandpipers and Redshanks have both been seen to carry young between their legs to transport them over obstacles such as walls.

Some species run from danger. Cream-coloured Coursers may freeze with necks out stretched along the ground or they may run, suddenly stopping to stand erect to look for sources of disturbance. Others take to flight. Woodcocks will suddenly take flight, climbing steeply and make a clattering sound as they rise through the trees. This sudden movement will surprise a ground predator making it pause.

Similarly, Snipes when disturbed take a low zig-zag flight, making them difficult quarry for both raptors and shooters. When feeding in deep water, Redshanks will habitually swim from danger and may even, like Moorhens, dive to hide.

Anti-predator displays are not always so defensive. Defence may sometimes take the form of attack, particularly where there is strength in numbers among colonially or semi-colonially nesting birds and where the adults are not cryptically coloured. Oyster-catchers can be very aggressive in defence of their nests. When gulls, skuas or crows fly over, the Oystercatcher launches its attack, flying beneath the intruder and attacking with the bill, sometimes even forcing the bird to the ground. Even raptors will be attacked. Five pairs of Oystercatchers were seen to make a concerted attack on a Peregrine by flying at it in a tight flock and driving it away from their breeding grounds. Ground predators will be attacked by

The male Oystercatcher guards the mate throughout the incubation, protecting her from the attentions of other males.

Oystercatchers with a flight that it is similar to the butterfly-display and which acts as an avian hue-and-cry drawing the attention of other birds in the area to the presence of the predator.

The aggression of the Spur-winged Plovers in defence of their eggs and young is extreme. Both sexes are antagonistic towards intruding human beings and domestic animals, but males have the edge. They fly up with sharp metallic calls and will often be joined by adults from neighbouring territories.

REACHING MATURITY

Breeding maturity in waders may be reached within one to four years, depending on the species. Conclusive information is not available for all wader species, but many of the smaller species mature within a year. However, there may be differences between the sexes in the year of first breeding. Female sandpipers tend to breed in their first year as do some males, but others may wait up to three years. Thus, male Dunlins and Temminck's Stints may breed in their first, second or third years. Larger waders usually take longer to reach maturity: two years for godwits, Turnstones and probably for Curlews; three years for Stone Curlews; and four years for Oystercatchers. There are, however, examples of individuals maturing sooner.

As with other birds, despite the defensive activities of the parents, the period from egg-laying to fledging is dangerous and the losses of chicks are high. Calculating fledging success is not easy, because the young disperse and their habitat is often well-covered with vegetation. Various averages between 30 per cent and 80 per cent have been put forward for fledging success, but it may be less than 30 per cent in some species and in some circumstances. Sudden cold spells and heavy rain within the first week or so of hatching can be fatal.

The number of birds that die in the first year can be as great as the number lost in the weeks before fledging. More than half of the Curlews that fledge in Britain do not survive as long as a year. First-year mortality of Redshanks and Temminck's Stints is about 50 per cent.

Avocets from the populations around the North Sea and Baltic Sea suffer a first-year mortality of almost two-thirds. A 36 per cent first-year mortality in Oystercatchers is less than in other waders, but they do take four years to reach breeding condition by which time the mortality since fledging has reached 84 per cent. Mortality among second-year Oystercatchers is still high and John Goss-Custard suggests that young birds submit to older birds in finding food and that food shortage also contributes to mortality. Younger birds are also likely to have peripheral positions in roosting flocks which makes them more susceptible to cold through wind-chill and consequently some die.

As breeding maturity is reached the survival rate is high. In Oystercatchers it is 94 per cent and it is, therefore, not surprising that this species has been recorded as one of the longest living wild birds with one individual reaching 35 years 11 months and 16 days. Other waders do not approach this age, but it must be remembered that information about bird mortality is related to ringing recoveries and is therefore biased by the historical activities of ringers. Many species reach their late teens and it is probable that many exceed 20 years, a barrier which Avocets and Lapwings have both broken.

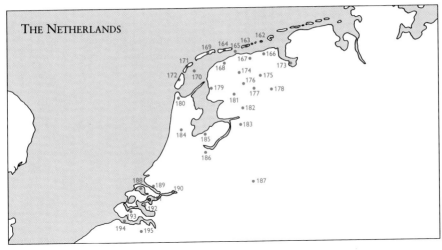

THE NETHERLANDS

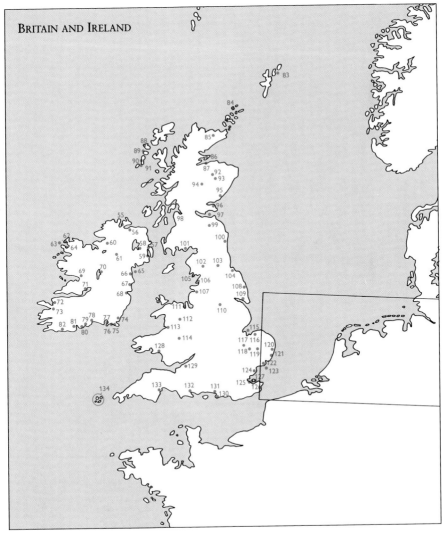

BRITAIN AND IRELAND

Key to map

BUL.	Bulgaria	SLOV.	Slovakia
CRO.	Croatia	TUN.	Tunisia
CZ.	Czech Republic		
D.	Denmark		
ES.	Estonia	•	Wader-
GR.	Greece	⌒	watching sites
H.	Hungary		
ICE.	Iceland		Boundary of
IS.	Israel		the Western
P.	Portugal	⁄	Palearctic

GAZETTEER

Waders can be seen throughout the region in suitable places, but their general affinity for wet and open habitats does restrict them. Many choose boggy moorland, wet-meadows and coastal marshes for breeding and spend the winter in sub-Saharan wetlands migrating via the coasts and estuaries of Europe.

There is a huge passage of migrating waders in autumn and a smaller but still large passage on the way north in spring. There are two main routes: the east Atlantic flyway down the west side of Europe and north Africa, and the eastern route via the Caspian and Black Seas, Turkey, Israel and Egypt. In addition to the wintering and passage waders found on the deltas of the Mediterranean region, there are several species that breed on these wetlands and waders that have specialized in breeding inland on steppe-grassland and the farmland which has replaced much of it.

This gazetteer makes no claim to being comprehensive. It is arranged from north to south in four sections corresponding to those marked on the map on pages 127 and 128–9: Iceland and Scandinavia, Northern Europe and Russia, Southern Europe and Turkey, and North Africa and the Middle East. The number preceding each entry refers to its location on the map.

ICELAND AND SCANDINAVIA

Iceland

The base-rock of Iceland is basalt and part of this large island is still volcanic. The lowlands are dwarf-scrub moorland, grassland and sedge-bog. Upland areas are often boggy, and above 600 m there is a high alpine zone of dwarf shrubs, herbs and mosses.

The breeding populations of Golden Plovers, Purple Sandpipers, Dunlins, Snipes, Black-tailed Godwits (members of the Icelandic race which are recognizable from their deeper rusty-red plumage and shorter bills), Whimbrels, Redshanks and Red-necked Phalaropes

are very large. Large numbers of Knots, Sanderlings and Turnstones pass through on migration.

1 Mývatn Shallow eutrophic lake with many islands, fed by cold and thermal springs. Important for its breeding ducks and waders such Golden Plovers and Dunlins.

2 Hjaltastasblá Marshes with streams, ponds and peat-bogs with breeding ducks, Dunlins, Whimbrels and Red-necked Phalaropes.

3 Breidafjördur Large area of coastal waters with thousands of islets and islands. Breeding Grey Phalaropes and passage waders, particularly Knots feeding on intertidal zones in spring.

4 Löngufjörur Estuarine coast. Large numbers of Knots, Sanderlings, Dunlins, Redshanks and Turnstones on

Purple Sandpipers breed in Iceland and Scandinavia and winter around the coasts of Iceland, western Norway and Scotland.

passage. Wintering Oystercatchers and Purple Sandpipers.

5 Leirárvogar Shallow estuarine bay with passage Knots and Dunlins. Wintering Oystercatchers and Purple Sandpipers.

6 Gardskagi Intertidal flats, rocks and beaches. Large number of passage waders including Knots, Sanderlings, Dunlins and Turnstones.

7 Skardsfjördur Brackish coastal lagoon with intertidal flats. Passage waders include about 1000 Ringed Plovers, over 1000 Knots and 10,000 Dunlins.

8 Stokkseyri Small coastal wetland with fresh-water and brackish ponds

and intertidal flats. Breeding Oystercatchers, Ringed Plovers and Grey Phalaropes.

9 Skúmsstadavatn Shallow fresh-water lake, ponds and sedge-marsh with breeding Snipes, Black-tailed Godwits, Redshanks and Red-necked Phalaropes.

Norway

Only 3 per cent of Norway is under cultivation and three-quarters of the country is mountainous. In the north above the tree-line is Arctic tundra. To the south and west are woodlands, mainly spruce and pine. The coastline is rugged with many deep fjords and many islands.

Among the breeding waders are 28,000 pairs of Dotterels, 1400 pairs of Great Snipes, 9500 pairs of Red-necked Phalaropes and significant numbers of Ruffs and Golden Plovers. The rocky coasts are ideal for large numbers of wintering Purple Sandpipers.

10 Varangerfjord Arctic shore important for wintering wildfowl and waders: 1800 Little Stints, 1000 Curlew Sandpipers and 10,000 Dunlins in autumn, 1000 Purple Sandpipers in winter and 500 Red-necked Phalaropes in spring.

11 Havmyran Open mire with small lakes. Important breeding area for waders, particularly Golden Plovers, Dunlins and Whimbrels.

12 Smøla Archipelago Hundreds of small islands and skerries with huge areas of shallow water, mire and heathland on island of Smola. Breeding Golden Plovers and Ruffs.

13 Dovrefjell High mountain with marshy valleys. Over 400 pairs of breeding Great Snipes and 200–400 pairs of Golden Plovers.

14 Akersvika Shallow bay on eastern side of Lake Mjosa with wet grassland and carr. Spring passage includes Golden Plovers, Ruffs, Curlews, Spotted Redshanks and Wood Sandpipers.

15 Dokkadeltaet Delta at end of Randsfjorden. Important for wader passage including Ruffs and Wood Sandpipers.

16 Hardangervidda Largest mountain plateau in Europe with about 5000 pairs of breeding Dotterels, about 10,000 pairs of Golden Plovers, about 100 pairs of Great Snipes, and Wood Sandpipers.

17 Nordre Øyeren Inland delta draining into shallow lake surrounded by deciduous woodland, grassland and farmland.

18 Ilene and Presterødkilen Wetlands Shallow marine bays with mud-flats. Lapwings, Wood Sandpipers and Ruffs on passage.

19 Øra Large estuary with extensive reedmarsh. Black-tailed Godwits breed. Most numerous passage waders are Ruffs and Dunlins.

Sweden

This large country is dominated by mountains in the north-west with lowlands around the Baltic coast. There are lakes throughout the country. Deciduous woodland and heath are the dominant habitats of the coastal fringe, but most of the country's woodland is coniferous with some oak and hazel in the south. There are peatbogs and alpine zones in the north.

The coastal areas with their adjacent beaches, marshes and islands are important for breeding waders, such as Avocets, Black-tailed Godwits and Ruffs, and for migrating waders. The lakes and surrounding bogs are breeding areas for three species of snipes and Red-necked Phalaropes. The bogs in the forest and mountain zones have breeding Broad-billed and Wood Sandpipers, Temminck's Stints and Golden Plovers.

20 Taavavuoma Marshes, rivers, streams, lakes and pools in depression in plateau in Swedish Lappland. Breeding waders include Ringed and Golden Plovers, Dunlins, Broad-billed Sandpipers, Ruffs, Jack Snipes, Bar-tailed Godwits, Spotted Redshanks and Red-necked Phalaropes.

21 Lake Laidaure Delta of River Rapaaldavens where Wood and Common Sandpipers and Red-necked Phalaropes breed.

22 Lake Tjålmejaure and Laisdalen Valley Two converging valleys with lakes and a river. Breeding Purple and Broad-billed Sandpipers, Great Snipes and Red-necked Phalaropes. It is the last staging post for many migrant waders on their way to breeding grounds further north.

23 Vindelfjällen Extensive mountains with patchwork of mires, lakes, valleys and rivers where Purple Sandpipers, Ruffs, Snipes, Great Snipes and Red-necked Phalaropes are among the ten breeding species of waders.

24 Lake Gammelstadsviken Shallow eutrophic lake with breeding Ruffs, Snipes, Redshanks, Wood Sandpipers and Red-necked Phalaropes. Passage migrants include Curlew and Broad-billed Sandpipers, both godwits and Spotted Redshanks.

25 Umeälven Delta This delta is constantly changing shape and is surrounded by wet-meadows where Black-tailed Godwits may breed. A staging post for migrants including Temminck's Stints, Ruffs, Jack Snipes, Black-tailed Godwits, Whimbrels, Green Sandpipers and Red-necked Phalaropes.

26 Lake Annsjön This very shallow lake is surrounded by marsh and a

Temminck's Stints breed in northern Scandinavia and Russia.

sandy ridge along 2 km of its shoreline. Among the 14 species of breeding waders are Temminck's Stints, Broad-billed Sandpipers, Curlews and Red-necked Phalaropes. It is also a staging post for spring migrants on the last leg of their journey north.

27 River Dalälven Broad stretches of river bordered by lagoons, arable and woods. Curlew Sandpipers and 250 pairs of Spotted Redshanks breed.

28 Stockholm Archipelago The breeding birds of these largely uninhabited islands include 100 pairs of Turnstones.

29 Lake Östen A shallow productive lake in flat landscape at which up to 1000 Ruffs and occasional Great Snipes may be seen.

30 Dättern Almost enclosed bay of Lake Vanern – reed-fringed shoreline with grazing meadows. Breeding Ringed Plovers and Black-tailed Godwits.

31 Lake Hornborgasjön Shallow lake edged by grazed pastures. Breeding Dunlins, Ruffs, Lapwings, Redshanks, Spotted Redshanks and Wood Sandpipers. Up to 3000 Ruffs pass through on passage.

32 Lake Tåkern Shallow eutrophic lake with extensive reedmarsh and wet-meadows. Breeding Oystercatchers, Dunlins, Ruffs and Redshanks.

33 Lake Kävsjön and Store Mosse Fresh-water lake and bog where Golden Plovers, Dunlins, Ruffs, Jack Snipes, Redshanks and Wood Sandpipers breed.

34 Gotland coast Low-lying peninsulas and islands to east of Gotland. Breeding Avocets, Ringed Plovers, Dunlins, Ruffs, Black-tailed Godwits, Curlews and Turnstones.

35 Getterön Island joined to mainland by embankment. Marshy vegetation and grazed coastal meadows. Breeding Avocets, Dunlins, Ruffs, Black-tailed Godwits and Redshanks.

36 Öland Large island with sandy beaches and low cliffs around the coasts and woodland inland. Breeding Avocets, Ringed Plovers, Dunlins, Lapwings, Ruffs, Black-tailed Godwits, Curlews, Redshanks and Turnstones breed. Large wader passage.

37 River Helgeån Lakes and farmland near Kristianstad with breeding Dunlins, Ruffs and Black-tailed Godwits.

38 River Klingavälsån and Lake Klankesjön Shallow, eutrophic lakes, streams, reedmarsh and wet-meadows. Lapwings, Dunlins, Snipes, Black-tailed Godwits, Curlews and Redshanks breed. Passage migrants include Ruffs, Spotted Redshanks, Greenshanks and Wood Sandpipers.

39 Bay of Foteviken Shallow coastal waters. Notable as a crossing point for raptors. Breeding waders include Oystercatchers, Avocets, Ringed and Kentish Plovers and Dunlins.

Finland

Although much of central and southern Finland is low-lying, the north is more hilly with deep river valleys and plateaux covered with tundra. There are 60,000 lakes in Finland. Taiga, peatlands and reedmarsh are among the habitats of the south.

The huge areas of habitats often support large numbers of breeding species at very low densities. Notable among the breeding waders are 100,000 pairs of Golden Plovers, 800 pairs of Dotterels, 8000 pairs of Broad-billed Sandpipers, 2000 pairs of Temminck's Stints and 10,000 pairs of Jack Snipes.

Spotted Redshanks breed in northern Scandinavia. They can sometimes be seen feeding in teams, moving in lines to disturb shoals of small fish.

40 Karigasniemi Tundra with peatbogs and dwarf birch. Breeding Broad-billed Sandpipers, Spotted Redshanks, Temminck's Stints, Whimbrels, Dotterels, Golden Plovers and Red-necked Phalaropes.

41 Koitilaiskaira Area of peatlands and birchwoods with streams and small pools. Ruffs, Jack Snipes, Spotted Redshanks, Wood Sandpipers and Red-necked Phalaropes breed.

42 Martimoaapa-Lumiaapa Bog with several ponds and lakes. Breeding Broad-billed Sandpipers, Jack Snipes. Redshanks and Red-necked Phalaropes.

43 Patvinsuo National Park Large peatland bogs and pools around Lake Suomujarvi. Breeding Broad-billed Sandpipers and Jack Snipes.

44 Valsörana-Björkögrunden Shallow areas of sea with archipelagos of 100 islands and islets. Breeding Turnstones and Redshanks. On migration route through Gulf of Bothnia.

45 Preiviikinlahden Extensive sea bay important for passage small sandpipers and other waders.

Denmark

This low-lying country has an extensive coastline in both the North and Baltic Seas. Over 90 per cent of the land surface has been cultivated, but there are some remaining peatbogs, heathland and sand-dunes.

The extensive intertidal areas have internationally important populations of wintering and passage waders. The wet-meadows and marshes provide breeding habitat for 3500–4700 pairs of Avocets and 600–800 pairs of Black-tailed Godwits. Up to 60 pairs of Wood Sandpipers breed.

46 South Laesø This large island in Kattegat has breeding Avocets, Ruffs, Curlews and Wood Sandpipers. Wintering waders include 600 Avocets and 45,000 Dunlins.

47 Ulvedybet and Nibe Bredning An internationally important site for waders including up to 400 pairs of breeding Avocets and large numbers of wintering waders including 300 Avocets, 10,000 Golden Plovers, 1000 Little Stints and 13,500 Dunlins.

48 Arup Holm and Hovsør Røn Shallow seashore and grazed meadows with breeding Avocets, Oystercatchers, Ringed Plovers, Lapwings, Dunlins and Redshanks and wintering Golden Plovers, Lapwings and Ruffs.

49 Hantsholm Reservatet Extensive sandy, coastal heath with lakes. Breeding Golden Plovers and Wood Sandpipers.

50 Agger Tange and Krik Vig A peninsula with brackish lagoons, salt-marsh and grazing meadows where Avocets, Black-tailed Godwits and Ruffs breed. Avocets, Golden Plovers, Little Stints and 20,000 Dunlins winter.

51 Nissum Bredning Shallow fjord with coastal lagoons and marshes with breeding Avocets and 15,000 Golden Plovers.

52 Nees Sund/Vilsund Coastal straits with brackish and saline lagoons, salt-marsh and tidal flats

where Avocets breed and up to 25,000 Golden Plovers winter.

53 Nissumfjord Shallow brackish fjord, coastal salt-marsh, reedmarsh and heath with breeding Avocets, Dunlins, Ruffs and Black-tailed Godwits. Maximum counts of wintering waders include 891 Avocets, 8690 Golden Plovers, 10,345 Lapwings, 14,163 Dunlins, 9715 Bar-tailed Godwits and 3028 Curlews.

54 Ringkøbing Fjord Shallow brackish bay with 400–450 pairs of breeding Avocets and 130–180 pairs of Black-tailed Godwits. Up to 10,000 Golden Plovers and 1000 Little Stints on passage or in winter.

NORTHERN EUROPE AND RUSSIA

Ireland

The lowlands of Ireland form a central plain surrounded by a perimeter of mountains. Peatbogs dominate the land not farmed or under forest. The farmland is predominantly pasture.

The island is important for its wintering wildfowl and waders which use the sheltered bays and estuaries. Oystercatchers, Grey Plovers, Knots, Sanderlings, Dunlins, the Icelandic race of Black-tailed Godwits, Bar-tailed Godwits, Curlews and Redshanks all winter in internationally important numbers on Irish estuaries, while the concentrations of Golden Plovers, Lapwings and Curlews which winter on the damp grassland further inland are also important North American vagrants are found on the west coast.

55 Lough Swilly Long, narrow sea inlet with wintering Oystercatchers, Lapwings, Dunlins, Curlews and Redshanks.

56 Lough Foyle Bay with salt-water marshes and mud-flats. Wintering Oystercatchers, Golden Plovers, Lapwings, Bar-tailed Godwits, Curlews and Redshanks.

57 Belfast Lough Sea lough with tidal mud-flats. Wintering Oystercatchers (*c*.10,000), Redshanks (*c*.3000) and Turnstones (*c*.11,500).

58 Lough Neagh and Lough Beg Lakes with marsh and meadow. Breeding Lapwings, Snipes, Curlews and Redshanks.

59 Strangford Lough Large bay with mud-flats, salt-marsh and islands. Average maximum of 46,600 waders winter here or pass through including 5000 Oystercatchers, Golden Plovers, Lapwings, Knots, Dunlins, Curlews and Redshanks.

60 Lower Lough Erne Indented shoreline bordered by marshes and wet-meadows. Breeding Snipes, Curlews and Redshanks.

61 Upper Lough Erne Flooded drumlins making islands and bays with wet pasture. Breeding Snipes (630 pairs or more), Curlews and Redshanks.

62 Termoncarragh Lake Coastal lagoon with sand dunes, beaches, machair and marshland. Breeding Red-necked Phalaropes (the only regular Irish site), Lapwings, Dunlins, Snipes and Redshanks. Red-necked Phalaropes on passage.

63 Inishkea Islands Breeding Lapwings, Oystercatchers and Dunlins. Wintering Golden Plovers, Sanderlings, Purple Sandpipers and Turnstones.

64 Blacksod Bay Large shallow bay with wintering Oystercatchers, Ringed Plovers, Sanderlings, Dunlins, Bar-tailed Godwits, Curlews and Redshanks.

65 Dundalk Bay Extensive sea bay. Up to 27,000 Oystercatchers, up to 26,000 Golden Plovers, Knots, Dunlin (up to 15,000), Black-tailed Godwits, Bar-tailed Godwits, Curlews and Redshanks. 57,000 wintering waders.

66 Boyne Estuary Long, narrow estuary with salt-marsh near the mouth. Wintering Icelandic Black-tailed Godwits, Oystercatchers, Golden Plovers, Lapwings, Knots, Dunlins, Curlews and Redshanks.

67 Malahide Estuary Estuary of River Broadmeadow. Wintering Oystercatchers, Golden Plovers, Knots, Dunlins, Curlews and Redshanks.

68 North Bull Island Sand-dune system in Dublin Bay, 5 km long and 1 km wide. 30,000 wintering waders include Oystercatchers, Grey Plovers, Knots, Sanderlings, Dunlins, Bar-tailed Godwits, Black-tailed Godwits, Curlews and Redshanks.

69 Rahasane Turlough Karst lake with marshes and seasonally flooded wet-meadows. Wintering waders include Golden Plovers (3000 with up to 15,000), Northern Lapwings (1500), Icelandic Black-tailed Godwits (up to 1100), Curlews (600) and Redshanks (up to 360).

70 Shannon Callows Flood-plain of River Shannon. Very important for both breeding and wintering waders. Breeding Lapwings, Snipes, Curlews and Redshanks. Wintering Golden Plovers, Lapwings, Icelandic Black-tailed Godwits and Curlews.

71 Shannon and Fergus Estuary Large estuary complex with 50,000 wintering and passage waders inc Oystercatchers, Golden Plovers,

Lapwings, Knots, Dunlins, Icelandic Black-tailed Godwits, Bar-tailed Godwits, Curlews, Redshanks and Spotted Redshanks.

72 Akeragh Lough Extensive shallow coastal lagoon. Up to 10,000 Lapwings and 4000 Curlews and regular American vagrants in autumn.

73 Castlemine Harbour Large shallow tidal area with 11,000 wintering waders include Oystercatchers, Golden Plovers, Knots, Sanderlings, Bar-tailed Godwits, Curlews and Redshanks.

74 Wexford Slobs Reclaimed land on either side of estuary. Large numbers of wintering wildfowl and wintering waders include Oystercatchers, Golden Plovers, Lapwings, Dunlins, Icelandic Black-tailed Godwits, Bar-tailed Godwits, Curlews, Spotted Redshanks and Redshanks.

75 Tacumshin Lake Coastal lagoon. Wintering Oystercatchers, Golden Plovers, Grey Plovers, Lapwings, Dunlins, Icelandic Black-tailed Godwits, Bar-tailed Godwits and Curlews.

76 The Cull/Killag Estuary, salt-marsh and reclaimed pasture. Wintering Oystercatchers, Ringed Plovers, Golden Plovers, Grey Plovers, Lapwings, Knots, Dunlins, Icelandic Black-tailed Godwits, Bar-tailed Godwits, Curlews and Redshanks.

77 Bannow Bay Sea bay with 16,000–20,000 wintering waders including Oystercatchers, Lapwings, Golden Plovers, Knots, Dunlins, Black-tailed Godwits, Bar-tailed Godwits, Curlews and Redshanks.

78 Dungarvan Harbour Large sea bay with wintering Golden Plovers, Knots, Dunlins, Icelandic Black-tailed Godwits, Bar-tailed Godwits, Curlews and Redshanks.

79 Blackwater Estuary Small estuary with Icelandic Black-tailed Godwits, Golden Plovers, Dunlins and Curlews.

80 Ballymacoda Estuary of River Womanagh, marshy fields and salt-marsh. Wintering Golden Plovers, Grey Plovers, Lapwings, Dunlins, Icelandic Black-tailed Godwits, Bar-tailed Godwits, Curlews and Redshanks.

81 Cork Harbour Large sheltered bay with up to 28,000 waders including Oystercatchers, Lapwings, Golden Plovers, Dunlins, Icelandic Black-tailed Godwits, Bar-tailed Godwits and Redshanks.

82 Inner Clonakilty Bay Tidal bay important for Icelandic Black-tailed Godwits. Other waders include Golden Plovers, Lapwings, Dunlins, Bar-tailed Godwits, Curlews and Redshanks.

Britain

The islands which make up Britain are all influenced by the sea. There is over 11,000-km of coastline and nowhere is more than 115 km from tidal waters. The shallow coastal waters into which over 120 estuaries drain are warmed by the Gulf Stream to create highly productive coastal waters.

Ornithologically, Britain is important for its colonies of breeding seabirds, the species on its peat and heather moorlands and for the estuaries which support huge numbers of wildfowl and waders, migrating along the east Atlantic flyway. More than a quarter of the North Sea's salt-marshes are found in eastern England. About 96 per cent of the EU's Golden Plovers breed on British moorlands. British and Northern Irish estuaries are staging posts or wintering grounds for over one and a half million waders.

A party of Dotterels pauses on low chalk hills in Cambridgeshire on their way north from North Africa to Scotland.

101 Solway Firth Large estuary with mud-flats and salt-marshes, grassland and arable farmland. Important for wintering wildfowl and waders with average winter maxima of 34,100 and 70,028. Waders include Oystercatchers (averaging 26,500 but reaching 40,000), Ringed Plovers, Knots (*c.*7000), Sanderlings, Bar-tailed Godwits (*c.*3250), Curlews (*c.*5000), Redshanks (*c.*2000) and Turnstones.

98 Inner Clyde Estuary Salt-marsh and tidal mud-flats. Average winter maximum for waders is *c.*12,000 with *c.*4400 Oystercatchers and *c.*3000 Redshanks.

91 Loch Hallan Shallow machair loch on South Uist with extensive reedbeds, marshes and machair. Breeding Oystercatchers, Ringed Plovers, Lapwings, Dunlins, Snipes and Redshanks.

90 Na Meadhoinen Iar Largest machair system in Britain, including Loch Druidibeg. 245 breeding pairs of Oystercatchers, 450 pairs of Ringed Plovers, 500 pairs of Lapwings, Dunlins, Snipes and Redshanks.

88 Balranald Marshes, small lochs, salt-marsh, machair, estuary and mud-flats. Breeding Oystercatchers, Ringed Plovers, Lapwings, Dunlins,

139

Woodcocks eat plant material, such as blackberries, as well as invertebrates. Birds from eastern and northern Europe move south and west in autumn.

Snipes and Redshanks. Wintering Ringed Plovers and Sanderlings.

89 Baleshare and Kirkibost Islands with lochs, marshes, intertidal flats, sand dunes and salt-marsh. Breeding Ringed Plovers, Oystercatchers, Lapwings, Dunlins, Snipes and Redshanks.

84 South Westray Coast Low rocky shore with sandy bays. Wintering Sanderlings, Purple Sandpipers and Turnstones.

830 Fetlar Heather moorland, grass-heaths, fresh-water lochs and marshes. Breeding Golden Plovers, Whimbrels (70 pairs) and Red-necked Phalaropes.

85 Flows of Caithness and Sutherland Huge undisturbed peat mire. Very important for breeding birds including over 500 pairs of Golden Plovers, 2600 pairs of Dunlins and over 1000 pairs of Greenshanks.

86 Cromarty Firth Large estuary with salt-marshes and extensive mud and sand-flats. Wintering Curlews, Bar-tailed Godwits and Redshanks.

87 Findhorn Bay Bay with salt-marsh and mud-flats. Wintering Oystercatchers (*c.*5000), Knots, Bar-tailed Godwits, Curlews and Redshanks.

92 Cairngorms Extensive uplands with high plateaux, snow beds, lochs, marshes, peatbog and moorland. Breeding Golden Plovers and Dotterels.

93 Caenlochan Tundra vegetation, moorland and marshes. Dense breeding population of Golden Plovers and important site for Dotterels.

95 Montrose Basin Estuarine basin with extensive salt-marsh and mud-flats. Average winter maximum for waders is 11,146 and includes Oystercatchers, Redshanks and Knots.

94 Drumochter Hills Moorland including blanket bog. Golden Plovers, Dotterels, Dunlins and Greenshanks breed.

96 Eden Estuary Small estuary with mud-flats, salt-marsh and shingle. Average winter maximum for waders is 12,356, among them Grey Plovers.

97 Firth of Forth Large estuary with beaches, salt-water marshes, mud-flats and sand dunes. Average winter wader maximum is 36,415, including Oystercatchers, Bar-tailed Godwits, Redshanks, Knots and Turnstones.

97 Moorfoot Hills Moorland and marshes. Important for breeding waders in Golden Plovers, Dunlins, Snipes and Curlews.

100 Northumbrian coast Mud-flats and salt-marshes along a stretch of coast from Berwick-upon-Tweed to Tynemouth. Nationally important for wintering and passage wildfowl and waders, including Ringed, Golden and Grey Plovers, Purple Sandpipers, Sanderlings, Bar-tailed Godwits and Turnstones.

102 Bollihope, Middleton, Abbotside, Askrigg and Mallerstang Commons and Bowes Moor Managed moorlands with wet flashes. Important for upland breeding waders such as Golden Plovers, Dunlins, Snipes, Curlews and Redshanks.

103 Teesmouth Extensive mud-flats, sand dunes and salt-marshes. Average

winter maximum for waders is 16,640, including Knots, Redshanks, Sanderlings and passage Ringed Plovers and Greenshanks.

104 Shap Fell Moorland with blanket bog. Breeding Golden Plovers, Dunlins, Snipes, Lapwings, Curlews and Redshanks.

105 Duddon Estuary Estuary with sand-flats, salt-marsh and dunes. Average winter maximum is 21,628.

106 Morecambe Bay Very large bay with mud-flats, salt-water marshes, salt-marsh and beaches. Oystercatchers and Redshanks breed. Average winter maximum is 143,552, most notable of which are almost 50,000 Oystercatchers, 13,000 Lapwings, 25,000 Knots, 5000 Bar-tailed Godwits and 9000 Curlews.

107 Ribble and Alt Estuaries Salt-water marshes, salt-marsh, mud-flats and wet-meadows. Average winter maximum for waders is 78,438 with 8000 Oystercatchers, 16,000 Dunlins, 10,000 Bar-tailed Godwits and 1000 Black-tailed Godwits on passage.

108 Derwent Ings Flooded grassland. Breeding Lapwings, Curlews, Snipes, Redshanks, Little Ringed Plovers and Common Sandpipers.

109 Humber Estuary Extensive estuary with mud-flats and salt-marshes. Very important for numbers of wintering waders with average maximum of 83,127, including Ringed, Golden and Grey Plovers, Knots, Sanderlings, Dunlins, Curlews and Redshanks.

110 Peak District National Park Moorland with breeding Golden Plovers, Dunlins and Curlews.

111 Dee Estuary Vast estuary with sand-flats, mud-flats and salt-marshes.

Breeding Lapwings and Redshanks. Average winter maximum for waders is *c*.83,000, including 30,000 Oystercatchers, 20,000 Knots and 5000 Redshanks.

112 Berwyn Moorland with blanket bog. Golden Plovers breed.

113 Dyfi Estuary Estuary with mud-flats, salt-marsh and raised bog. Breeding waders include Common Sandpipers and Redshanks. Passage includes Bar-tailed Godwits and Curlews.

114 Elenydd-Mallaen Moorland plateau with blanket bog and acid grasslands where Golden Plovers, Dunlins, Snipes, Curlews and Common Sandpipers breed.

115 The Wash Vast intertidal area with mud-flats, sandbanks, salt-marshes and sandy beaches. Internationally important staging post with an average maximum for waders is *c*.153,000.

116 North Norfolk Coast Sand dunes, shingle islands, beaches, salt-marsh, damp pasture, much of which is nature reserves. Breeding Oystercatchers, Avocets, Ringed Plovers. Passage includes Avocets, Sanderlings, Black-tailed Godwits, Ruffs, Spotted Redshanks, Greenshanks, Wood and Green Sandpipers. Reserves at Titchwell, Snettisham and Cley are particularly good for wader-watching.

117 Nene Washes Rough grassland and wet pasture with breeding Snipes, Redshanks and Black-tailed Godwits.

118 Ouse Washes Grassland subject to floodwater storage in winter when Lapwings, Snipes and Black-tailed Godwits may be seen alongside huge numbers of wildfowl. Damp, grazed pasture in summer is excellent for

breeding ducks and waders include Ruffs, Black-tailed Godwits, Snipes and Redshanks.

119 Breckland Heaths Heathland and sandy farmland with about 100 pairs of Stone Curlews breeding.

120 Minsmere–Walberswick Large reedmarshes and both fresh-water and salt-water lagoons. Breeding Avocets. Well-placed hides at Minsmere and extensive management have made it an excellent site for watching passage waders.

121 Havergate–Orford Ness Estuary complex with mud-flats and salt-marsh. Breeding Avocets, Redshanks and Snipes. Passage waders including Avocets, Ruffs and godwits.

122 Stour and Orwell Estuaries Mud-flats and salt-water marshes. Average winter maximum for Stour is *c*.25,000 and for Orwell is *c*.18,000 includes Bar-tailed Godwits and Grey Plovers.

123 Hamford Water Estuary with tidal creeks, mud-flats and salt-marsh. The average winter maximum for waders is *c*.12,000.

124 Blackwater, Colne and Dengie Marshes Estuaries with mud-flats and salt-marshes. Breeding Ringed Plovers and Redshanks. Average winter maximum for waders is *c*.47,000.

125 South Thames Marshes Salt-water marshes, salt-marsh, mud-flats and wet-meadows. Average winter maximum for waders is about 82,000 including tens of thousands of Oystercatchers, Knots and Dunlins.

126 Medway Marshes Salt-water marshes, salt-marsh, mud-flats and wet-meadows. Average winter maximum of waders is 24,000.

127 The Swale and South Sheppey Estuary with grazing marshes, mud-flats and salt-marsh. Breeding Ringed Plovers, Lapwings and Redshanks. Average winter maximum for waders is about 83,000.

128 Burry Inlet Estuary with dunes, salt-water marsh and mud-flats. The average winter maximum for waders is about 36,000.

129 Severn Estuary Mud-flats, salt-water marshes, salt-marsh, wet-meadows and grassland. Average winter maximum for waders is about 53,000. Also important passage of Iceland/Greenland breeders.

130 Pagham Harbour Natural harbour with salt-marsh and tidal mud-flats. Average winter maximum for waders is *c.*24,000 including Grey Plovers, Ruffs, Black-tailed Godwits, Spotted Redshanks and Greenshanks.

131 Chichester and Langstone Harbours Two large natural harbours with 60-km shoreline with fresh-water lagoons, salt-marshes and mud-flats. Average winter maxima of waders for Chichester is 41,037 and for Langstone is 37,444. Passage waders include Black-tailed Godwits, Greenshanks and Spotted Redshanks.

132 Poole Harbour Large natural harbour with several fresh-water lakes and brackish lagoons and water-meadows. Oystercatchers, Avocets, Redshanks, Curlews, Black-tailed Godwits, Spotted Redshanks and Ruffs.

133 Exe Estuary Salt-water marshes and mud-flats. Average maximum in winter for waders is *c.*13,000 including Avocets, Oystercatchers, Ringed Plovers and Black-tailed Godwits.

134 Isles of Scilly Islands with various coastal habitats, including rocky shores, mud-flats, sand-flats and lagoons. Oystercatchers breed. Wintering waders include Sanderlings,

Turnstones and Purple Sandpipers. Passage of waders includes American vagrants,.and 45,000 Dunlins.

Russia

Three broad vegetational zones occur across this large country in three bands: steppe, taiga and tundra. In the steppes in the south the breeding waders include Stone Curlews, Collared Pratincoles and Lapwings. Around lakes and boggy areas in the taiga there are breeding Ruffs, Great Snipes and Black-tailed Godwits. These species also occur in the tundra along with hundreds of thousands of breeding sandpipers.

136 Ainov Islands Two tundra islands with tens of pairs of breeding Red-necked Phalaropes.

137 Dubna Marshes Flood-plain of River Dubna with bogs, boggy forest, lakes and agricultural land. Black-tailed Godwits and Curlews breed.

138 Faustovo Flood-plains Water meadows, marshes and lakes. Breeding Ruffs (about 100 females), Great Snipes (40–50 breeding females), Black-tailed Godwits (100–200 pairs), Marsh Sandpipers (65–70 pairs) and Terek Sandpipers (10–15 pairs). Passage of 4000–5000 Golden Plovers, over 10,000 Ruffs and hundreds of Wood Sandpipers.

139 Burukshuniye Salt-lakes Chain of saline and brackish lakes and marshes. Post-breeding waterfowl include 50,000 waders.

Estonia

Extending from the Finnish Gulf and the shores of the Baltic Sea to the Gulf of Riga, this republic is a low-lying plain with many lakes. About a fifth of the country is forested with much of the rest either arable or diary farming.

139 Matsalu Bay Huge sea bay with salt-marshes, reedmarsh, grazing pastures and hay-meadows. Huge spring and autumn passage of wildfowl and waders includes several hundred thousand Ruffs.

140 Nigula Zapovednik Marsh with lakes. Breeding Golden Plovers, Green Sandpipers and Wood Sandpipers.

Latvia

Small, low-lying country on eastern shore of the Baltic Sea. Much of the country is farmed, but some bogs and

lakes, where waders breed, remain. A fifth of the country is forested.

141 Ollu and Kodu-Kapzemes Large bog almost unaffected by human activity. Breeding Golden Plovers, Whimbrels, Curlews, Redshanks and Wood Sandpipers.

142 Teičt Bog Large raised bog with numerous lakes and pools. Breeding Golden Plovers, Black-tailed Godwits, Whimbrels, Curlews, Redshanks and Wood Sandpipers.

Lithuania

Low-lying republic on on shores of Baltic Sea. Waders breed on some of the remaining bogs and lakes. Most

The Terek Sandpiper breeds in Russia and appears to migrate across the Mediterranean and the Sahara in one flight.

of the countryside is farmed and a fifth is forested.

143 Lake Kretuonas Eutrophic lake with islands and fresh-water marsh. Breeding Ruffs, Great Snipes and Black-tailed Godwits.

144 Čepkelai Marshes Extensive marshes with 22 small lakes and dunes. Breeding waders include Golden Plovers, Dunlins and Curlews.

France

France is one of the largest countries in the region. It has two separate coasts: the Atlantic/Channel and the Mediterranean. The most important wintering and passage sites for waders are the network of coastal wetlands, but there are inland breeding sites, particularly in the Loire Valley.

145 Bays and estuaries of the Somme, the Authie and the Canche Mud-flats, salt-marsh and estuaries with Ringed Plovers, 10,000–20,000 Golden Plovers, Sanderlings and Bar-tailed Godwits on passage. Wintering waders include 3000–7700 Oystercatchers, Avocets, up to 12,000 Dunlins and Curlews.

146 Estuary of the Seine Estuary with mud-flats, marshes and wet-meadows. Avocets, Ruffs and sometimes Black-winged Stilts breed. Passage of 5000 Avocets, 1000 Ringed Plovers, 100 Kentish Plovers, hundreds of Whimbrels, over 10,000 Redshanks. Wintering waders include 2000 Avocets and 1000 Curlews.

147 Baie des Veys Mud-flats, beaches, sand dunes, marshes and wet-meadows. Breeding Avocets, Black-tailed Godwits and Curlews. Passage includes over 1000 Ringed

Plovers and wintering waders include up to 10,000 Oystercatchers, 1000 Golden Plovers and 10,000 Dunlins.

148 Baie du Mont-St-Michel 22,000 ha of mud-flats and about 1000 ha of salt-marsh. Large wader passage includes 4000 Ringed Plovers, up to 10,000 Golden Plovers, up to 10,000 Dunlins and up to 10,000 Bar-tailed Godwits. Wintering waders include 10,000–20,000 Oystercatchers, up to 5000 Golden Plovers, 1500–3000 Grey Plovers, 3000–7000 Knots, 22,000–35,000 Dunlins, 1000–2000 Icelandic Black-tailed Godwits and 2000–5000 Curlews.

149 Golfe du Morbihan and Etier de Penerf Mud-flats, salt-marsh and salt-water lagoons with breeding Black-winged Stilts, Avocets and Redshanks. Passage includes Ringed Plovers, Whimbrels and Greenshanks. Wintering Avocets, Grey Plovers and 20,000–30,000 Dunlins.

150 Loire Valley Rivers, streams and farmland with breeding Stone Curlews and Little Ringed Plovers (over 1000 pairs) .

151 Sologne Lakes, marshes, woods and farmland with breeding Black-winged Stilts and 20,000 pairs of Lapwings.

152 Bay and marsh of Bourgneuf Salt-water and fresh-water lagoons, salt-marsh and mud-flats with Black-winged Stilts, Avocets, Lapwings, Black-tailed Godwits and Redshanks. Wintering birds include Avocets and Grey Plovers.

153 Marsh d'Olonne Salt-water lagoons and salt-marsh with breeding Black-winged Stilts and Avocets. Passage includes Black-winged Stilts, Avocets, thousands of Black-tailed Godwits and over 10,000 Whimbrels.

Dunlins and Sanderlings feed on the mud at the tide's edge while Bar-tailed Godwits, Redshanks and Curlews feed in shallower areas about to be uncovered or just covered by the tide.

154 Baie de l'Aiguillon Mud-flats, sand-flats and salt-marshes. Breeding Black-winged Stilts. Passage of Ruffs, 5000 Black-tailed Godwits and 20,000 Whimbrels. Wintering: 6000 Avocets, 2600 Grey Plovers, 10,000 Lapwings, 4000 Knots, 16,000 Dunlins, 6500 Icelandic Black-tailed Godwits and 1000 Bar-tailed Godwits.

155 La Brenne Lakes, marshes, woods, farmlands with breeding Black-winged Stilts and 10–20 pairs of Stone Curlews.

156 Val d'Allier River valley with uncultivated land, lakes, woodland, marshland and plains. Breeding birds include over 200 pairs of Stone Curlews and over 1000 pairs of Little Ringed Plovers.

157 Rochefort/Ile d'Oléron Bays, salt-water lagoons, salt-marshes and mud-flats. Breeding Black-winged Stilts, Avocets, Redshanks. Passage includes Black-tailed Godwits, Whimbrels, Black-winged Stilts. Wintering Avocets, Dunlins (up to 16,000), Grey Plovers and Knots.

158 Etangs and salins du Languedoc Salt-water lagoons and salt-marshes with breeding stilts, Avocets and Kentish Plovers.

159 Aigues-Mortes Lakes and saltpans with breeding Avocets (400 pairs), Black-winged Stilts, Stone Curlews and Kentish Plovers.

160 Camargue Large delta with beaches, sand dunes, salt lagoons and marshes. Breeding Black-winged

Stilts (more than 500 pairs), Avocets (650–800 pairs), Collared Pratincoles, Stone Curlews and Kentish Plovers (700 pairs). Large wintering and passage populations of waders.

161 Plaine de la Crau Semi-arid steppe meadows with 300 pairs of Stone Curlews.

Netherlands

Much of the country is flat and reclaimed from the sea or from marshland. Two-thirds is farmed. Very large tidal flats still exist on the Waddensee which extends from Denmark along the German North Sea coast to the Netherlands. The Netherlands' ornithological importance lies in its breeding, wintering and passage waterbirds. Among the waders the most important breeding birds are 90,000 pairs of Oystercatchers, 8000

pairs of Avocets, 200,000–275,000 pairs of Lapwings and 65,000 pairs of Black-tailed Godwits. The wintering and passage populations of Oystercatchers (300,000 birds in January), Avocets (18,000 in September), Golden Plovers (400,000 in November), Grey Plovers (17,000 in May), Knots (100,000 in September), Dunlins (24,000 in September), Bar-tailed Godwits (70,000 in May) and Curlews (100,000 in September).

The Waddenzee is very large, 2600 km², of which half is tidal flats ('wadden') and half is tidal channels and shallow water. A barrier of islands from Rottumerplaat to Texel, separates the Waddensee from the North Sea. Each winter 600,000–800,000 waders pass through the area and are found in greater density than on the German and Danish parts of the sea. When every 5–10 years, ice blocks much of the area the numbers of waders decrease. There are important breeding populations of Oystercatchers, Avocets, Lapwings, Curlews, Kentish Plovers, Black-tailed Godwits, Redshanks and Ruffs.

162 Rottumerplaat and Rottumeroog Uninhabited island nature reserves with breeding Oystercatchers and large numbers of wintering waders including 20,000 Oystercatchers, 20,000 Dunlins, 10,000 Knots, 6000 Curlews and 3000 Bar-tailed Godwits.

163 Schiermonnikoog Island with beaches, dunes, salt-marsh and wet-meadows. Avocets, Black-tailed Godwits, Ruffs and Redshanks breed. Other waders in winter and on passage include Oystercatchers and Dunlins in large numbers.

164 Ameland Island with beaches, dunes, salt-water lagoons, salt-marsh and wet-meadows. Avocets, Black-tailed Godwits, Ruffs and Curlews breed. Passage and wintering waders in large numbers.

165 Engelsmanplaat Island with salt-marsh and mud-flats. Large passage of waders.

166 Groningen buitendijks Salt-water marshes, mud-flats and raised salt-marsh. breeding Avocets. Up to 36,000 Oystercatchers on passage, 2600 Avocets, 5000 Golden Plovers, 27,000 Dunlins, 5500 Bar-tailed Godwits, 11,000 Curlews, 5500 Redshanks and 1100 Greenshanks on passage.

167 Lauwersmeer Dammed fresh-water estuary with salt-marsh, farmland and military training area. Breeding Oystercatchers, Avocets, Ruffs, Black-tailed Godwits and Redshanks.

168 Friesland buitendijks Mud-flats, salt-water marshes and raised salt-marsh with breeding Oystercatchers and Avocets. Waders on passage.

169 Terschelling Island with beaches, dunes, salt-water lagoons, salt-marsh and wet-meadows. Breeding Avocets, Black-tailed Godwits and Curlews.

170 Griend Small island with beaches, salt-marsh and mud-flats. Tens of thousands of Oystercatchers, Dunlins, Knots and Bar-tailed Godwits.

171 Vlieland Island with beaches, sand dunes, salt-water lagoons, mud-flats and grassland. Breeding waders include Avocets, Black-tailed Godwits and Curlews. Important for wintering and passage waders.

172 Texel Largest of the Frisian Islands with beaches, sand dunes, salt-water lagoons, fresh-water marshes, raised salt-marsh, wet-meadows and farmland. Avocets, Black-tailed Godwits, Redshanks and Ruffs breed. Wintering and passage Oystercatchers, Avocets, Kentish Plovers, Golden Plovers, Grey Plovers, Knots, Sanderlings, Dunlins, Bar-tailed Godwits, Curlews, Redshanks and Wood Sandpipers.

173 Dollard Estuary with salt-water marshes, coastal mud-flats and raised salt-marsh. Breeding Avocets, Ruffs, Black-tailed Godwits and Redshanks. Large wader passage including 6000 Avocets, 2800 Grey Plovers, 30,000 Dunlins, Bar-tailed Godwits, Curlews and Spotted Redshanks (*see also* Dollart (204) under Germany)

174 Groote Wielen Complex of fresh-water reedmarsh, alder/willow carr and wet-meadows. Breeding Ruffs, Snipes, Black-tailed Godwits and Redshanks.

175 Leekstermeer Fresh-water lake surrounded by peatbogs, pasture, marsh and reedmarsh. Breeding Ruffs, Lapwings, Snipes, Avocets and Redshanks.

176 Oude Venen and De Deelen Lakes, reedmarsh, wet-meadows. Breeding Ruffs.

177 Van Oordt's Mersken Wet grasslands and marshes. Breeding Ruffs, Black-tailed Godwits, Snipes, Curlews and Redshanks. Roosting waders include Black-tailed Godwits and Curlews.

178 Fochteloerveen, Esmeer and Huis ter Heide Raised bogs with heather moor, open water and sewage treatment plants. Breeding Black-tailed Godwits, Ruffs. Passage waders include 8000 Black-tailed Godwits and 10,000 Whimbrels.

179 Workumerwaard Foreshore, beaches, wet-meadows, reedmarsh and fresh-water marshes. Breeding Avocets, Ringed Plovers, Ruffs, Black-tailed Godwits, Redshanks. Non-breeding Avocets, Curlews and Black-tailed Godwits in large numbers.

180 Balgzand Large area of salt-water marshes, intertidal mud-flats and raised salt-marsh. 500 pairs of Avocets. Passage and wintering species include 18,000 Oystercatchers, Avocets, 24,000 Knots, 13,000 Dunlins, 10,000 Bar-tailed Godwits, Curlews, Spotted Redshanks and Greenshanks.

181 Tjeukemeer Large fresh-water lake with reedmarsh, swamp forest and grasslands. Ruffs, Black-tailed Godwits and Redshanks.

182 De Wieden and De Weeribben Shallow lakes, wet-meadows, peat lowlands and woods. Breeding Snipes, Black-tailed Godwits and Curlews.

183 IJsseldelta River, polders and two lakes. 2000 breeding pairs of Black-tailed Godwits and 350–400 breeding pairs of Redshanks.

184 Zuidelijk Poldergebied Vast polder complex of wet grasslands (12,600 ha). Breeding Lapwings (4000 pairs), Ruffs (100–200 pairs), Snipes (150–200 pairs), Black-tailed Godwits (4000 pairs) and Redshanks (1000 pairs).

185 Oostvaardersplassen and Lepelaarsplassen Complexes of shallow lakes, reedmarsh and woodlands. Breeding Avocets (250–400 pairs with up to 6000 seen regularly) and Black-tailed Godwits. Passage and wintering birds include 2000–5000 Ruffs and 5000–10000 Black-tailed Godwits.

186 Arkemheen, Zeldert and Eemmeer Wet grasslands and lake. Breeding Ruffs, Black-tailed Godwits and Redshanks.

187 Waal and Rijn Flood-plains Wet-meadows, marshes, slow-flowing rivers, clay-pits and arable. Breeding Ruffs, Black-tailed Godwits and Redshanks.

188 Grevelingen Semi-stagnant saline lake with dunes, beaches, islands and wet-meadows. Breeding Avocets, Ringed and Kentish Plovers, Black-tailed Godwits and Redshanks.

189 Haringvliet and Hollands Diep Reclaimed portion of Rijn/Maas estuary with breeding Avocets, Ruffs, Black-tailed Godwits and Redshanks.

190 Biesbosch Reclaimed portion of Rijn/Maas estuary with breeding Avocets, Black-tailed Godwits and Redshanks.

191 Krammer and Volkerak Reclaimed portion of Rijn/Maas with breeding Avocets, Ruffs, Black-tailed Godwits and Redshanks.

192 Ooterschelde Reclaimed estuary with salt-water and fresh-water lakes and intertidal flats. Breeding Avocets. Wintering and passage waders include 88,000 Oystercatchers, Avocets, Ringed and Kentish Plovers, 7000 Grey Plovers, 18,000 Knots, 58,000 Dunlins, 7000 Bar-tailed Godwits, 18,000 Knots, 10,000 Curlews, 1500 Spotted Redshanks, 900 Greenshanks and 1300 Turnstones.

193 Veerse Meer Brackish lake formed from part of reclaimed Schelde estuary. Breeding Avocets, Black-tailed Godwits and Redshanks.

194 Westerschelde Remnants of Schelde estuary. Important for breeding Avocets and Ruffs and wintering 17,000 Oystercatchers, 750 Avocets, 1900 Ringed Plovers, 1200 Kentish Plovers, 5200 Grey Plovers, 8500 Knots, 1500 Sanderlings, 35,000 Dunlins, 5600 Bar-tailed Godwits, 5000 Curlews, 250 Spotted Redshanks, 1000 Redshanks and 200 Wood Sandpipers.

195 Putting–Groot Eiland Damp grassland latticed by brackish creeks. Breeding Black-tailed Godwits, Snipes, Avocets and Redshanks.

Germany

Most of lowland Germany is farmed, but much of the mountainous south is still forested. The Baltic and North Sea shores are low and flat with bays, peninsulas and small islands.

The German Waddenzee is important for its wintering waders: 80,000 Oystercatchers, 40,000 Knots, 300, 000 Dunlins and 40,000 Curlews. The salt-marsh and meadows behind the tidal flats are important for their breeding waders including Avocets and Redshanks.

196 Sorge-Niederung Lowland area of wet-meadows and moorland with breeding Ruff, Black-tailed Godwits (220 pairs) and waders on passage including 20,000 Lapwings and 10,000 Golden Plovers in autumn.

197 Baltic coast Long expanse of flat sandy coasts, with brackish lagoons and coastal lakes with breeding Avocets, Black-tailed Godwits and Ruffs.

198 Westrugen–Hiddensee–Zingst Extensive coastal reserve with shallow water, islands, shore and salt-marsh. Breeding Avocets, Ruffs, Black-tailed Godwits and Redshanks. Passage includes Wood Sandpipers in autumn.

199 Greifswalder Bodden Bay with salt-marsh and seashore. 10,000 Lapwings on autumn passage.

200 Peenetalmoor and Anklamer Stadtbruch Wet peatbog with reedbeds, willow and birch woods. Breeding birds include Snipes, Black-tailed Godwits and Green Sandpipers.

201 Unteres Odertal Large dyked river, shipping canal and polders liable to flooding. Breeding Snipes and spring passage of 10,000 Lapwings, 1000 Ruffs, 1700 Snipes and 200 Wood Sandpipers.

202 Waddenzee Two-thirds of the 4500 km^2 is mud-flats and sand-flats with the remainder is sub-tidal rivers and creeks, saltings and islands. In the North Frisian Waddenzee reclamation has created saltings. Breeding Oystercatchers (1100 pairs), Avocets (3000 pairs), Ringed Plovers (1400 pairs), Kentish Plovers (900 pairs), Dunlins (30 pairs), Curlews (120 pairs) and Redshanks (7000 pairs). Passage waders include 150,000 Oystercatchers with 65,000 overwintering, 5000 Avocets, 10,000 Ringed Plovers, 25,000 Grey Plovers, 400,000 Dunlins,

1000–1500 Little Stints, 80,000
Bar-tailed Godwits, 2000 Whimbrels,
40,000 Curlews with 15,000
overwintering, 4000 Spotted
Redshanks, 3000 Greenshanks and
2000 Turnstones.

203 Hamme-Niederung Large area
of wet-meadows and oxbow lakes.
Passage and wintering waders include
Golden Plovers, 10,000 Lapwings,
Ruffs, Snipes, Black-tailed Godwits
and Curlews.

204 Dollart Part of the Waddenzee
whose wintering and passage migrants
include 19,000 Avocets, 1000 Grey
Plovers, 50,000 Dunlins, 2500
Black-tailed Godwits, 5000 Bar-tailed
Godwits and 1000 Spotted Redshanks
(*see also* Dollard (173) under
Netherlands).

205 Lower Ems Tidal mud-flats,
oxbow lakes, reedbeds, sedgebeds and
wet-meadows. Passage of 1100 Golden
Plovers, 220 Snipes and 1000 Black-
tailed Godwits.

206 Bastau-Niederung Large
peatbog with breeding Black-tailed
Godwits, Curlews and about 9000
Lapwings on passage.

**207 Zwillbrocker Venn and
Vredener Wiesen** Moors, heath and
wet-meadows in River Berkel basin.
Breeding Oystercatchers, Snipes,
Black-tailed Godwits and Curlews.

Poland

Only 9 per cent of Poland is over 300 m.
There are many lakes, particularly in the
north, and coastal lagoons on the Baltic.
Over a quarter of the country is still
wooded. Wetlands are still extensive
with fresh-water marshes and one and
a half million hectares of peatbogs (5
per cent of the country's land surface).

Waders breeding in internationally
important numbers are Ruffs, Great
Snipes and Black-tailed Godwits.
The wetlands are important for
passage waders.

208 Beka and Rewa Meadows
Coastal salt-marsh liable to flood in
autumn and winter. Breeding Dunlins,
Oystercatchers and Ruffs. Passage
waders include 2000 Golden Plovers.

209 Vistula Estuary Shallow estuary
with shallow pools. Over 30 species of
waders have been recorded on passage.

210 Biebrza Valley River valley
much of which is in natural state or
is reverting after nineteenth-century
drainage schemes. Breeding Ruffs
(about 150 females), Great Snipes
(about 150 displaying males) and
Black-tailed Godwits.

**211 Lower Narew Valley and
Zegrzynski Reservoir** Breeding
Black-tailed Godwits.

212 River Noteć Valley Flood-
meadows and low-lying peat bogs with
many ditches. Breeding Black-tailed
Godwits and Curlews.

213 Odra Valley and Lake Dąbie
120-km river valley with marshes,
peatbogs, flood meadows, oxbow
lakes. Breeding Oystercatchers, Ruffs
(650 males) and Green Sandpipers.

214 Słońsk Reserve Flood-plain
where Warta, Odra and Postomia
meet. Ruffs (10–30 pairs) and Black-
tailed Godwits (20–160 pairs).

215 Middle Warta Valley River
flood-plain. Breeding Ruffs, Great
Snipes, Black-tailed Godwits (600–700
pairs), Redshanks (250 pairs). Passage
waders include up to 3000 Ruffs and
3000–4000 Black-tailed Godwits.

216 Lower Bug Valley Dry pastures
with fens at mouths of tributaries.
Breeding Stone Curlews, Ringed Plovers,

Little Ringed Plovers, Lapwings, Snipes, Great Snipes (56 males across 13 sites), Black-tailed Godwits, Redshanks, Green and Common Sandpipers.

217 Liwiec Valley 140-km long river valley. Breeding Lapwings, Snipes, Great Snipes, Black-tailed Godwits and Common Sandpipers.

218 Vistula Valley Unregulated river between Deblin and Plock. Breeding Stone Curlews, Ringed Plovers, Little Ringed Plovers, Lapwings, Black-tailed Godwits and Common Sandpipers.

219 Nysa Reservoirs Significant passage of waders including Lapwings (6000), Little Stints, Dunlins, Ruffs, Wood and Common Sandpipers.

Czech Republic

The northern and southern borders are mountainous with arable and mixed woodland covering the remainder.for wader-watchers the extensive fish-ponds are of most interest.

220 Znojmo Farmland with small areas of dry grassland. Breeding Stone Curlews.

221 Lednice fish-ponds Five large fish-ponds with reedmarsh. Breeding Black-tailed Godwits. Passage include up to 500 Ruffs.

Slovakia

Mountains cover much of this recently created republic and most of the wader interest is in the south among the complexes of fish-ponds in the Danube Valley.

222 Záhorské močiare marshes Breeding Black-tailed Godwits plus migrants.

223 Jakubovské rybníky ponds Large numbers of migrants.

224 Senné Fish-ponds Fish-ponds on East Slovakian Plains. Breeding Black-winged stilts and Black-tailed Godwits.

Hungary

The Great Hungarian Plain, crossed by the Danube and Tisza Rivers, covers much of the central and southern part of the country with mountains to the north. Over 70 per cent of the land is farmed and 13 per cent is forested. the natural steppe with oak woodland was felled 300 years ago and replaced by farmed steppe-grassland.

Avocets, Collared Pratincoles and Black-tailed Godwits are among the breeding waders in the wetlands of the plain, where large numbers of waders rest on passage.

225 Fertö-tó Part of shallow, saline lake with reed and sedge vegetation, forming part of Neusiedler See. Breeding Black-tailed Godwits and Curlews.

226 Hanság Marsh and woodland with fish-ponds and grazing. Breeding Black-tailed Godwits and Curlews.

227 Hortobágy Extensive steppe with salt-lakes, water-storage tanks, fish-ponds, reed and fresh-water marshes. Breeding Avocets, Stone Curlews, Collared Pratincoles and Black-tailed Godwits. Large passage of waders and wildfowl with Dotterels, Ruffs (up to 50,000 in spring), Black-tailed Godwits (6000–10,000 in spring) and very rare Slender-billed Curlews.

228 Ócsa Peatbog with wet woodland, meadows, reedbeds and open water. Stone Curlews and Black-tailed Godwits breed.

229 Velence and Dinnyés South-western part of Lake Velence with salt-steppe and salt lake. Black-tailed Godwits breed. 20,000 Ruffs and 200

Black-tailed Godwits have been recorded on spring passage.

230 Kis-Balaton Part of Lake Balaton which has become a marsh with reedbeds and ponds. Breeding Avocets.

231 Pusztaszer Four riverine wetlands with fish-ponds, reedbeds and farmland. Breeding Avocets, Black-winged Stilts, Stone Curlews and Black-tailed Godwits. Spring passage of 9000 Ruffs and 1000 Black-tailed Godwits.

Ukraine

Once largely covered with steppe-grassland, the Ukraine is now extensively farmed for grain. A few isolated pockets of the original steppe survive. The most interesting areas for waders are sites on the Black Sea coast.

232 Lake Shatskiye Overgrown fresh-water lakes. Breeding Black-tailed Godwits.

233 Krivaya Peninsula Breeding waders include Black-winged Stilts, Avocets, Collared and Black-winged Pratincoles.

234 Obitochnaya Peninsula Coastal shallows and low shores with large passage of waders.

235 Molochny Liman Salt-lake with extensive shallows and islands. Breeding grebes, gulls, terns and waders. Slender-billed Curlews sometimes seen on passage.

236 Dunay and Yagorlytski and Tendra Bays Ukrainian part of Danube Delta (*see* also Romania) and two large sea bays separated by long spit from Black Sea. Breeding Avocets (500–800 pairs), Collared and Black-winged pratincoles. Several thousands of non-breeding Ruffs and Black-tailed Godwits oversummer. Slender-billed Curlews occur on passage.

SOUTHERN EUROPE AND TURKEY

Portugal

On the south-west of the Iberian peninsula, Portugal is a hilly country with low-lying coastal areas and broad, fertile river valleys. The mountainous hinterland still retains some oak forest, heathland and pine woods, but much has become maquis and garrigue. The southern plains are dry steppe-grassland, grazed by sheep or converted to arable, with some Mediterranean forest. The major estuaries are important for wintering waders, particularly Avocets, and as staging posts for passage waders.

237 Idanha-a-Nova Wheatfields and dry pasture, notable for steppe species including Stone Curlews.

238 Alter de Chão As above.

239 Monforte Plains As above.

240 Elvas Plains As above.

241 Tejo Estuary Vast expanse of mud-flats, salt-marshes and reedmarshes. Breeding Black-winged Stilts (200 pairs) and Collared Pratincoles (100 pairs). Important for passage and wintering waders including Avocets (9000 with a maximum of 18,000), Grey Plovers (5000 with a maximum of 9000), Dunlins (30,000), Curlew Sandpipers (1000 on passage), Black-tailed Godwits (7000 with a maximum of 12,200) and Redshanks (3000 with maximum of 5000).

242 Sado Estuary Vast mud-flats, sand-flats, salt-marshes with saltpans and fish farms. Breeding Black-winged Stilts and Collared Pratincoles. Wintering Avocets and Grey Plovers.

243 **Évora** Wheatfields and dry pasture. Steppe species including Stone Curlews breed.

244 **Moura–Safara** As above.

245 **Vidigueira–Beja** As above

246 **Castro Verde Plains** Fields and dry pasture, notable for steppe species including Stone Curlews.

247 **South-west coast** Mainly cliffs but also estuaries, sand-flats, salt-marsh and sand dunes. Black-winged Stilts and Stone Curlews breed.

248 **Quinto da Rocha** Saline and brackish marshes between the estuaries of the Alvor and Odiaxere. Breeding Black-winged Stilts, Kentish Plovers and Collared Pratincoles. Wintering Stone Curlews. Up to 21 species of passage waders have been recorded.

249 **Ria Formosa** Coastal lagoons, mud-flats, sand-flats and salt-marsh. Breeding Avocets, Black-winged Stilts, Collared Pratincoles and Kentish Plovers. Over 20,000 wintering and passage waders include Knots, Sanderlings, Turnstones, Avocets and Grey Plovers.

250 **Castro Marim** Complex of saltpans, reclaimed salt-marshes and tidal mud-flats. Breeding Black-winged Stilts, Avocets, Collared Pratincoles and Kentish Plovers.

Spain

Only Switzerland has a higher average altitude than Spain, most of which is at least 300 m above sea-level. The remaining steppe-grassland is ornithologically important and includes breeding Stone Curlews. Spanish coastal wetlands provide breeding sites for Black-winged Stilts, Avocets, Collared Pratincoles and Kentish

Plovers, in addition to staging posts for passage waders.

251 **Marismas de Santoña** Coastal marsh with sand dunes. Passage and wintering waders include Whimbrels and Curlews.

252 **Ría de Arosa** Small harbour with mud-flats. Wintering and passage waders include Grey Plovers.

253 **Parameras de Maranchón** High plateau with breeding Stone Curlews and other steppe birds.

254 **Ebro Delta** Brackish lagoons, salt-marshes, salt lakes, sandy beaches and rice paddies. 1000 pairs of Black-winged Stilts, 400 pairs of Avocets, 100 pairs of Collared Pratincoles, 1000 pairs of Kentish Plovers.

255 **Albufera de Alcudia** Large coastal lagoon, marshes and abandoned saltpans. Breeding Black-winged Stilts.

256 **Salobrar de Campos lagoons** Plain with small natural lagoons and saltpans. At least 100 pairs of Black-winged Stilts.

257 **Brozas** Wide plain between River Tajo and Sierra de San Pedro. Very good for steppe birds with over 1000 pairs of breeding Stone Curlews.

258 **Trujillo** Wide undulating plain with breeding steppe species including Stone Curlews.

259 **Zorita and Madrigalejo** Extensive undulating grasslands. Breeding Stone Curlews and Collared Pratincoles.

260 **La Serena** Extensive undulating grasslands. Of exceptional importance for steppe birds with thousands of breeding Stone Curlews and small colonies of Collared Pratincoles. Wintering Golden Plovers and Lapwings in tens of thousands.

261 **Albufera de Valencia** Fresh-water coastal lagoon with abundant

vegetation. Breeding Black-winged Stilts, Collared Pratincoles and Kentish Plovers.

262 Valley of Sierra de Alcudia Wide valley, consisting mainly of winter sheep pasture. Stone Curlews breed.

263 Lagoons of Pedro Munoz and Manjavacas Group of lagoons on River Zancara. Breeding Black-winged Stilts, Avocets, Collared Pratincoles and Stone Curlews on surrounding farmland.

264 Campo de Montiel Stony plain with patches of garigue and grassland. Steppe breeders include Stone Curlews.

265 Pétrola-Almansa-Yecla Undulating plain with arable, dry

grassland and maquis. Numerous breeding Stone Curlews.

266 Santa Pola Salinas Saltworks in natural lagoon. Breeding Black-tailed Godwits, Avocets and Kentish Plovers. Wintering and passage Avocets.

267 Isla Cristina Marshes Coastal marshes on Guadiana estuary. Passage and wintering waders include Kentish Plovers.

268 Ría de Huelva Large coastal marshes at estuaries of Tinto and Odiel. Breeding Black-winged Stilts and Avocets. Important for passage waders including Sanderlings.

269 Coto Doñana and Guadalquivir Marshes Large and important complex

Sanderlings scamper along the tide's edge in search of food. They migrate along western European coasts to Africa.

of estuarine marshes. At least 1000 pairs of Black-winged Stilts, 3560 pairs of Avocets, hundreds of pairs of Collared Pratincoles and 500 pairs of Kentish Plovers. Wintering and passage waders including Black-tailed Godwits.

270 Bay of Cadiz Shallow bay with wide intertidal zone. Several hundred pairs of Black-winged Stilts, Avocets and Kentish Plovers. Wintering Avocets, Ringed Plovers and Kentish Plovers.

271 Salinas of Cabo de Gata 15-km coastal strip with saltpans and steppe. Breeding Avocets and Black-winged stilts. Passage waders.

272 Islets of Lanzarote Rocky islands with breeding seabirds and Stone Curlews.

273 Llanos de la Mareta Scrub and grasslands on Lanzarote with breeding Stone Curlews and Cream-coloured Coursers.

274 Costa Punta Lima Sandy beaches, mud-flats and sand-flats. Important feeding area for waders include Ringed Plovers, Kentish Plovers, Grey Plovers, Sanderlings, Dunlins, Bar-tailed Godwits, Whimbrels, Redshanks and Turnstones.

275 Jable de Lajares Sandy plain. Breeding Stone Curlews and Cream-coloured Coursers.

276 Jable de Corralejo Sand dunes and sandy beaches. Breeding Stone Curlews and Cream-coloured Coursers.

277 Península de Jandía Semi-arid massif. Breeding Stone Curlews and Cream-coloured Coursers.

Italy

The Italian peninsula has a considerable climatic variation, from the cool temperate north to the warm south with its almost rainless summers, resulting in four major geographical and vegetational zones. The Alps in the north have mixed forest and meadows. In the north-east the Po Valley, Italy's largest area of lowland, has deciduous forest and pasture. The Appenines still have large areas of forest, but has been cleared for farming. The coastal area is maquis and garigue. The 5000-km coastline is a mixture of dunes, lagoons and cliffs. Despite the Italians' reputation as bird killers, many of the major estuaries and coastal lagoons are important for passage and wintering wildfowl and waders.

278 Venetian Lagoons Extensive coastal lagoons with tidal mud-flats. Breeding Black-winged Stilts, Avocets and Redshanks. Spring passage has Spotted Redshanks, Ruffs and Marsh Sandpipers.

279 Po Delta Vast delta with tidal estuaries, reedbeds, lagoons, fishponds, sandy beaches and farmland. Breeding Oystercatchers (the entire Italian population of 15 pairs), Black-winged Stilts and Kentish Plovers.

280 Vasche dell'Eridania Ponds, wet grassland and arable. Breeding Black-winged Stilts. Migrating Common and Wood Sandpipers.

281 Valli di Comacchio Shallow lagoons, salt-marshes and canals with breeding Black-winged Stilts (200 pairs), Avocets (200 pairs), Collared Pratincoles, Kentish Plovers (100 pairs) and Redshanks. Slender-billed Curlews have been recorded on passage.

282 Punte Alberete and Valle della Canna Extensive wetland in flood-plain of Po north of Ravenna. Breeding Black-winged stilts.

283 Salina di Cervia Saltpans derived from coastal lagoons. Breeding Black-winged Stilts (70 pairs),

Avocets (100 pairs) and Kentish Plovers (100 pairs).

284 Lake Massaciuccoli and Arno and Serchio Estuaries Complex of marshes and estuaries with a shallow lake fringed with reedbeds. Breeding Black-winged Stilts, Collared Pratincoles and Stone Curlews.

285 La Trappola Brackish marsh. Breeding Stone Curlews. Passage waders include up to 700 Black-tailed Godwits in a day.

286 Orbetello Lagoon and Lake Burano Coastal lagoon and fresh-water lake. Breeding Black-winged Stilts and Stone Curlews. Passage of Black-tailed Godwits and at least one Slender-billed Curlew has been recorded in recent years.

287 Gulf of Manfredonia Wetlands, now largely fishponds and saltpans. Breeding Black-winged Stilts, Avocets (over 50 pairs), Kentish Plovers (over 100 pairs). Wintering Avocets (5000) and Curlews.

288 Stagno di Pilo and Stagno di Casaraccio Lagoons, marshes and saltpans. Breeding Stone Curlews and wintering wildfowl and waders.

289 Altopiano di Campeda Grassland. Stone Curlews breed.

290 Sinis Peninsula and Gulf of Oristan Coastal lagoons and lakes. Breeding Back-winged Stilts, Avocets, Kentish Plovers and Collared Pratincoles. Kentish Plovers, Dunlins and Little Stints are among the wide range of wintering waders.

291 Cagliari Wetlands Complex of fresh water and saltpans with breeding and wintering Avocets and Black-winged Stilts. Wintering waders.

292 Stagnone di Marsala and Saline di Trapani Lagoon and saltpans. Breeding Black-winged Stilts and

Kentish Plovers. 21,000 waders on spring passage and about 3000 Kentish Plovers in August.

293 Pantani di Capo Passero Complex of shallow saltpans with breeding Black-winged Stilts and Kentish Plovers. Passage waders include 5000 Kentish Plovers in autumn, 6000 Little Stints in autumn, 4500 Curlew Sandpipers in spring, 8000 Ruffs in spring, Marsh Sandpipers and 3000 Wood Sandpipers.

Croatia

Much of Croatia is lowland and the major river valleys are forested. The Dalmatian coast can be important for passage migrants when the weather is harsh in central Europe.

294 Kopački Rit Flood-plain of Danube and Drava with extensive reedmarsh, fishponds and oxbows. Large numbers of waders on passage include Ruffs, Wood and Green Sandpipers, Greenshanks and Black-tailed Godwits.

295 Bokanjacko and Nin Saltpan Farmland with marshes, reedbeds, ditches and saltpans. About 200 Ruffs occur here in spring.

296 Neretve Delta Complex of estuary, marshes, coastal lagoons, salt-marsh and wet-meadows crossing border into Bosnia Herzegovina. Breeding waterbirds, wintering ducks and grebes, and passage of waders has included Slender-billed Curlews.

Romania

Romania can be divided into three main physical zones. One-third is mountains, one-third hills and plateaux, and the remaining third plains. The plains are mainly farmland with oak woods, steppe-woodland and in the south-east steppe. Wetlands occur along the Danube, with a major marshland complex at its delta.

297 Cefa Fish-ponds Passage of Spotted Redshanks in autumn.

298 Sînpaul Ponds Fish-ponds with extensive reedmarsh. Wader passage includes in spring Marsh and Wood Sandpipers.

299 Danube Delta Major,and very threatened complex of marsh and riverine habitats. Notable for breeding waterbirds. Breeding waders include Black-winged Stilts, Avocets, Collared and Black-winged Pratincoles, Stone Curlews and Marsh Sandpipers. Also passage waders including Black-tailed Godwits and Slender-billed Curlews.

300 Lake Taşaul Large brackish lake with marsh. Passage waders include Ruffs and Avocets.

Bulgaria

Much of the lowland has been converted to agriculture, but a third of the country is still forested. There are wetlands along the Black Sea coast and the banks of the River Danube. Black-winged Stilts, Avocets and Collared Pratincoles breed along the coast.

301 Lake Durankulak Brackish to fresh-water coastal lake with reedmarsh. Breeding Collared Pratincoles.

302 Yatata Reservoir Former sedimentation reservoir. Breeding Black-winged stilts and Avocets.

303 Lake Atanassovo Complex of saltpans with settling pools and reedbeds. Breeding Black-winged Stilts, Avocets (725 pairs), Stone Curlews and Collared Pratincoles. Up to 7000 Avocets on autumn passage.

304 Lake Burgas Brackish to fresh-water lake with belt of reeds. Breeding Black-winged Stilts, Avocets and Collared Pratincoles.

305 Lake Mandra Brackish coastal lake used as reservoir and surrounded by wet-meadows and marshes. Breeding Black-winged Stilts and Avocets.

Greece

Greece has a long, rugged sea-coast and many islands in the surrounding Ionian, Aegean and Mediterranean Seas. The mainland is mountainous with lowlands in narrow coastal bands and river floodplains. The ornithological importance of Greece lies in her breeding raptors and waterfowl, which include 1000 pairs of Black-winged Stilts, 700 pairs of Avocets and 1900 pairs of Collared Pratincoles. Large numbers of Avocets winter in the Evros Delta and the Gulf of Amvrakikos.

306 Lake Kerkini Fresh-water reservoir and marshes. Black-winged Stilts breed and passage includes 2900 Avocets, over 5000 Ruffs and 8000 Black-tailed Godwits.

307 Porto Lagos Lakes and Lagoons Coastal brackish and fresh-water lakes with breeding Black-winged Stilts (100 pairs), Avocets and Spur-winged Plovers. Second most important place in Greece for passage Slender-billed Curlews. 1500 wintering Avocets.

308 Lake Mitrikou Natural, fresh-water lake, surrounded by reedbeds. Breeding Black-winged Stilts, Avocets, Collared Pratincoles and Spur-winged Plovers.

309 Evros Delta Major wetland threatened by several problems. Breeding waders include Black-winged

Spur-winged Plovers breed in northern Greece, Turkey, Israel and the Nile Valley.

Stilts, Avocets, Stone Curlews, Collared Pratincoles, Kentish Plovers and Spur-winged Plovers. Small numbers of Slender-billed Curlews on passage in spring.

310 Nestos Delta Brackish coastal lagoons with Black-winged Stilts, Avocets, Stone Curlews, Collared Pratincoles and Spur-winged Plovers.

311 Axios, Loudias and Aliakmon Estuaries Black-winged Stilts, Avocets, Stone Curlews, Collared Pratincoles and Redshanks breed. Passage of 20,000–50,000 waders includes 6000 Curlew Sandpipers, 3000 Ruffs, 4000 Black-tailed Godwits, 4000 Spotted Redshanks and, sometimes, Slender-billed Curlews.

312 Epanomi Lagoon Small coastal lagoon surrounded by salt-marsh, heathland, coast and farmland.

Breeding Black-winged Stilts, Avocets, Stone Curlews and Collared Pratincoles.

313 Alyki Lagoon, near Kitros Coastal lagoons with islands and salt-marsh. 20 pairs of Black-winged Stilts, 10–50 pairs of Avocets, 10–15 pairs of Stone Curlews and 100 pairs of Collared Pratincoles.

314 Agios Mamantos Marsh Coastal salt-marsh with brackish lake that dries in summer. Breeding Black-winged Stilts, Avocets (300 pairs), Collared Pratincoles (100 pairs), Stone Curlews, Kentish Plovers and Redshanks. Passage of waders.

315 Kalamas Estuary Delta of mud-flats. Breeding Black-winged Stilts, Stone Curlews and Collared Pratincoles.

316 Gulf of Amvrakia Complex of brackish lagoons, sandy coastal strips, salt-marsh, reedbeds and mud-flats. Important wetland site whose breeding waders include Black-winged Stilts (over 3000 pairs), Stone Curlews (30 pairs) and Collared Pratincoles (over 150 pairs).

317 Gulf of Kalloni Large sea bay with shallow brackish zones, small fresh-water marshes, salt-marshes and saltpans. Breeding Black-winged Stilts, Stone Curlews and Collared Pratincoles.

318 Mesolongi and Aetoliko Lagoons Wetland complex with salt-marsh, mud-flats and sandbanks. Black-winged Stilts, Avocets, Stone Curlews and Collared Pratincoles breed. Waders include occasional Slender-billed Curlews on passage.

319 Alyki Lagoon, Aegion Coastal lagoon, which dries out in summer, with some reeds and salt-marsh. Black-winged Stilts, Ruffs and Wood Sandpipers occur on passage.

320 Marathon Marshes Shallow lakes and reedmarsh behind the village of Marathon. Passage migrants include Ruffs and Marsh Sandpipers.

Turkey

This large country is partly in Europe and partly in Asia. On the European side of the Sea of Marmara the oak forest has largely been replaced by steppe. On the southern shore and along the coast of the Black Sea some forests of beech, oak and spruce persist, but much of the land is cultivated. The Aegean region is largely maquis, while the Mediterranean region is dominated by the Toros Mountains with their wooded slopes. Anatolia is composed of mountains and plateaux. Much of the forest hads given way to steppe.

There are several important wetlands on river deltas and inland lakes. Although the ornithological importance of the wetlands lies mainly in their breeding populations of Pygmy Cormorants, Dalmatian Pelicans, Marbled Teals and White-headed Ducks, it has significant populations of Avocets, Collared Pratincoles and Spur-winged Plovers.

321 Kizihrmak Delta Large wetland with extensive reedmarsh. Breeding Black-winged Stilts, Stone Curlews and Collared Pratincoles. Autumn passage of waders includes Greenshanks.

322 Kavak Delta Small delta with marshland. About 100 pairs of Collared Pratincoles and Kentish Plovers breed. Passage waders include Marsh Sandpipers.

323 Kocasu Delta Habitats include maquis, pasture, lakes, dunes and farmland. Breeding Black-winged Stilts, Stone Curlews and Collared Pratincoles.

324 Manyas Gölü Lake surrounded by farmland and some reedmarsh. Stone Curlews and Spur-winged Plovers breed.

325 Apolyont Gölü Large lake with several islands and large wet-meadows and reedmarsh on south-western shore with farmland on other shores. Breeding Collared Pratincoles and Spur-winged Plovers (55 pairs).

326 Çamalti Tuzlasi Extensive coastal area of bays, salt-marshes with lagoons and reedmarsh. Black-winged Stilts, Avocets, Spur-winged Plovers. Wintering waders include Little Stints.

327 Acigöl Very salty lake, which becomes salt-swamp in summer with marshes around fresh-water springs. Black-winged Stilts and Avocets breed. Up to 6000 Avocets in October.

Greenshanks and Spotted Redshanks will sometimes work together in small flocks, walking side-by-side and feeding on small animals that they disturb.

328 Bafa Gölü and Menderes Delta
Slightly saline lake, alluvial plains with tamarisk, estuary with lagoons and cotton fields. Breeding Oystercatchers, Black-winged Stilts, Avocets, Stone Curlews, Collared Pratincoles and Spur-winged Plovers. Wintering Avocets and Black-tailed Godwits, Curlews and Marsh Sandpipers on passage.

329 Kulu Gölü Steppe lake with small islands. Oystercatchers, Avocets, Black-winged Stilts, Greater Sandplovers breed. Stilts, Avocets, Kentish Plovers, Little and Temminck's Stints and Stone Curlews occur in late summer and autumn.

330 Bolluk Gölü Highly saline lake with warm springs. Important breeding site for gulls, terns and waders including Oystercatchers and Avocets. Passage includes Golden Plovers.

331 Sultan Marshes Brackish lakes, fresh-water lakes, reedmarsh and saltpans. Breeding Black-winged Stilts, Avocets, Collared Pratincoles, Greater Sandplovers and Spur-winged Plovers. Passage Avocets, Spotted Redshanks, Little Stints and Black-tailed Godwits.

332 Karapinar Ovasi Huge plain with saltpan in centre. Breeding Black-winged Stilts, Avocets, Stone Curlews,

Collared Pratincoles, Greater Sandplovers and Redshanks.

333 Hotamiş Sazhği Fresh-water marsh. Breeding waders include Black-winged Stilts, Stone Curlews, Collared Pratincoles, Greater Sandplovers, White-tailed Plovers and Spur-winged Plovers. Passage and wintering waders include Avocets, Little Stints, Ruffs, Black-tailed Godwits, Spotted Redshanks and Marsh Sandpipers.

334 Ereğli Sazhği Large wetland with lake and marshes. Important for breeding waterbirds including Black-winged Stilts, Avocets, Stone Curlews, Collared Pratincoles, Spur-winged Plovers and Greater Sandplovers. Passage waders include Little Stints and Black-tailed Godwits.

335 Cukurova Four river deltas, lakes of various sizes, salt-marshes and extensive dunes. Breeding Black-winged Stilts, Stone Curlews, 3000 pairs of Kentish Plovers, Spur-winged Plovers. Large numbers of passage and wintering migrants: up to 21,000 Avocets, Greater Sandplovers, 10,000 Little Stints, Broad-billed Sandpipers, up to 2500 Ruffs and Black-tailed Godwits.

336 Goksu Delta Estuary with two brackish lagoons, salt-steppe, reedmarsh and scrub-covered dunes.

Their habit of picking parasites from the backs of basking sea mammals has given Grey Phalaropes the name 'whale-birds'.

Breeding Black-winged Stilts, Avocets, Stone Curlews, Collared Pratincoles and Spur-winged Plovers. Passage waders including Little Stints, Ruffs and Marsh Sandpipers.

337 Upper Murat Vadigi Flood plains with wet grassland. Oystercatchers, Black-winged Stilts and Redshanks.

338 Bendimahi Delta Fresh-water marsh where river enters Van Golu. Breeding Oystercatchers, Black-winged Stilts, Avocets, Stone Curlews and Redshanks.

339 Arin Golu Saline lake surrounded by arable. Oystercatchers, Black-winged Stilts, Avocets and Redshanks breed. Passage including up to 2000 Redshanks, 1000 Black-winged Stilts and 2000–3000 Little Stints.

340 Ercek Gölü Brackish lakes with steep and rocky shores to north and west and shallow shores with mud-flats to south and east. Breeding Oystercatchers, Black-winged Stilts, Avocets, Stone Curlews and Redshanks. Up to 2000 Avocets and up to 900 Red-necked Phalaropes in May.

341 Van Marshes Small lagoons alongside Van Gölü. Breeding Black-winged Stilts, Avocets and Redshanks.

Cyprus

This large island has been extensively cultivated, but forest remains in the wilder western parts of the Troodos Mountains and the Kyrenia range. Maquis remains in parts of the east

and on coastal promontories. There are no perennial rivers and the important wetlands are salt lakes at Akrotiri and Larnaca with man-made lakes to the south of the Troodos Mountains. The salt lakes and coastal plains provide habitat for passage and wintering waders.

342 Paphos Plain Narrow coastal plains. Resting place for passage migrants including Collared and Black-winged Pratincoles and Spur-winged Plovers. Wintering Stone Curlews.

343 Akrotiri Salt lake. Breeding Black-winged Stilts. Greater Sandplovers and Marsh Sandpipers on passage.

344 Larnaca Four connected salt lakes. Breeding Black-winged Stilts. Passage waders include Avocets, Ruffs and Broad-billed, Wood and Marsh Sandpipers. Wintering Stone Curlews.

NORTH AFRICA AND THE MIDDLE EAST

Morocco

The western end of the Rif Mountains runs across the north of Morocco. Four mountains run across the country from south-west to north-east, reaching 4000 m in the High Atlas. Along the Atlantic coast are lagoons that are important elements of the East Atlantic Flyway for migrating waders.

345 Karriet Arkmane Saltpans and salt-marsh. Kentish Plovers and Black-winged Stilts both breed and occur on passage alongside other waders including Little Stints, Wood Sandpipers, Greenshanks and Black-tailed Godwits.

346 Merja Zerga Large shallow lagoon which is surrounded by wet grassland and marshes. Its huge passage of migrants includes Black-tailed Godwits, Little Stints, Greenshanks, Spotted Redshanks, Wood Sandpipers. Small numbers of wintering Slender-billed Curlews.

347 Sidi Moussa-Oualidia Salt-marsh, saltpans, reclaimed farmland and a lagoon at the mouth of the River Azemmour. An occasional site for small numbers of Slender-billed Curlews in autumn. Other passage waders include Avocets, Collared Pratincoles, Black-tailed Godwits, Curlew Sandpipers and Ruffs.

348 Middle Atlas Lakes Small, shallow lakes to the north-east of Ifrane. Passage of waders including Black-winged Stilts, Avocets, Little Ringed Plovers, Black-tailed Godwits and Greenshanks.

349 Puerto Cansado Coastal lagoon which is very important for wintering and passage waders. Among 100,000 wintering waders are huge flocks of Dunlins, Knots and Redshanks. 8000 Little Stints winter here as have occasional Slender-billed Curlews.

Mauritania

Only half of this large country falls within the Western Palearctic. Much of the area is desert with steppe-grassland along the coast and across the south of the country. It does, however, have a wetland site of world importance.

350 Banc d'Arguin National Park covering extensive tidal flats (50 km²). A little short of a third of the seven million waders wintering in West Africa do so here.

Tunisia

The highest ground in Tunisia is the saharan Atlas, which covers most of the country apart from the lowland coastal fringe. Cereals are grown at the eastern tip of the Atlas, on the south of which some forest remains. olives are grown on the coast near Sfax. The rest of the country is steppe, merging into desert and semi-desert with a vast salt lake at Chott el Djerid. Breeding waders include Cream-coloured Coursers and Collared Pratincoles.

351 Lake Ichkeul Large lake into which five rivers drain and which is connected to the sea, providing water which ranges from fresh to saline. Black-winged Stilts and Kentish Plovers breed. Large numbers of waders gather in autumn and spring, including Avocets, Temminck's and Little Stints, Curlew Sandpipers, Marsh Sandpipers, Ruffs and Greenshanks.

352 Lake of Tunis (or Lac de Tunis) Large lake south of Tunis. Large numbers of wintering waterbirds at southern end. Large passage of waders.

353 Sfax Saltpans Massive saltworks along the coast from Sfax to Thyna and coastal mud-flats. Black-winged Stilts and Redshanks breed. Large

Cream-coloured Coursers breed in the desert fringes of north Africa and in the Canary Islands.

numbers of wintering and passage waders including curlews, godwits, Dunlins and Marsh Sandpipers. The Gulf of Gabes, on which these saltpans are situated, contains half of the waders wintering in the Mediterranean.

354 Djebel Tebaga Semi-desert typical of the area. Cream-coloured Coursers breed in this habitat.

Egypt

Physically this large country is divided into three distinct areas: the Western Desert, the fertile Nile Valley and the mountainous desert in the east. It is in the Nile Valley that breeding and passage waders are most likely to be found. Senegal Thick-knees and Spur-winged Plovers breed along the banks.

355 Lake Burullus Shallow brackish lake in the Nile Delta connected to the sea by a narrow outlet. Sand-flats and marsh. Southern shore dominated by saltpan and fish-ponds. Breeding waders include Painted Snipes, Collared Pratincoles, Spur-winged Plovers and Kittlitz's Plovers. Migrants on passage.

356 Lake Manzala Largest lake on Nile Delta. Shallow and brackish. Connected to sea by outlet 5 km west of Port Said. Fish-ponds, marsh and sand-flats. Breeding Painted Snipes, Collared Pratincoles, Kittlitz's Plovers, Kentish

In Egypt, the population of Kittlitz's Plovers is sedentary, breeding and wintering along the banks of the Nile and on grassy plains.

The female Painted Snipe begins her courtship standing laterally to her mate. She stands with one wing raised and spread and the other folded. As the display becomes more intense she turns to face the male and brings forward her wings so that the carpal joints are in line with her head.

Plovers and Spur-winged Plovers. Migrants on passage.

357 Lake Idku Shallow lake to east of Alexandria. Connected to sea. Lake margins and shores reed-fringed. Painted-snipe may breed. Collared Pratincoles, Kentish Plovers and Spur-winged Lapwings breed.

358 Lake Maryut Once a very fertile lake it is now suffering from pollution. Extensive reedmarsh and salt-marsh to the west. Breeding Painted Snipes, Collared Pratincoles, Kittlitz's Plovers, Kentish Plovers and Spur-winged Plovers.

Israel

For such a small country Israel has a large number of species both breeding and passing through. The variety of habitats is the reason for the variety of breeding species and its geographical position is the reason for the numbers migrating through the country. The main habitats in which waders are found here are the desert edge, farmland and wetlands, represented by fish-pond complexes and salt-pans.

359 Hula Nature Reserve Remnant of extensive marshes. Breeding Black-

Sociable Plovers migrate in flocks from Russia and Kazakhstan to north-east Africa and south-west Asia.

winged Stilts, Collared Pratincoles and Spur-winged Plovers. Passage of waders including Broad-billed and Marsh Sandpipers, Black-tailed Godwits and Sociable Plovers.

360 Maagan Mikhael and Ma'yan Zevi Large complex of fish-ponds. Breeding Spur-winged Plovers and Black-winged Stilts. Migrants include Temminck's Stints.

361 Bet She'an Valley Fish-ponds and pools where waders and other water-birds stop to feed, the numbers varying with water-levels. Avocets breed.

362 Nahal Habosar Nature Reserve In Negev Desert with desert edge and irrigated farmland. Breeding Cream-coloured Coursers and Stone Curlews. Wintering Sociable Plovers and Dotterels.

363 Eilat Saltworks, sewage works and farmland on the migration route where the Arava Valley meets the Red Sea. Passage of waders includes Collared Pratincoles, Cream-coloured Coursers, Caspian, Sociable and Spur-winged Plovers, Greater Sandplovers, Broad-billed and Marsh Sandpipers.

BIBLIOGRAPHY

Barnard, C.J. and Thompson, D.B.A., *Gulls &
Plovers: The Ecology and Behaviour of Mixed
Species Feeding Groups*, Croom Helm,
Beckenham, 1985

Barnes, R., *Coasts and Estuaries*, Hodder &
Stoughton, London, 1979

Bent, A.C., *Life Histories of North American
Shore Birds*, Dover, New York, 1962

Birkhead, T.R. and Moller, A.P., *Sperm
Competition in Birds*, Academic Press, London,
1991

Brooke, M. and Birkhead, T.R., *The Cambridge
Encyclopedia of Ornithology* Cambridge
University Press, Cambridge, 1991

Burton, P.J.K., *Feeding and Feeding Apparatus in
Waders*, British Museum (Natural History),
London, 1974

Campbell, B. and Lack, E., *A Dictionary of
Birds*, Poyser, Calton, 1985

Cramp, S. and Simmons, K.E.L., *Handbook of the
Birds of Europe, the Middle East and North
Africa*, Oxford University Press, Oxford, 1983

Elkins, N., *Weather and Birds*, Poyser, Calton,
1985

Evans, P.R., Goss-Custard, J.D. and Hale, W.G.,
Coastal Waders and Wildfowl in Winter,
Cambridge University Press, Cambridge, 1984

Ferns, P.N., *Bird Life of Coasts and Estuaries*,
Cambridge University press, Cambridge, 1992

Furness, R.W., 'Wader populations at
Musselburgh', *Scottish Birds* 7 (1973) 275

Gooders, J., *Where to Watch Birds in Britain and
Europe*, Helm, Bromley, 1988

Goss-Custard, J.D., 'Feeding Ecology of the
Redshank', *Ibis* 111 (1988) 338–356

Grimmett, R.F.A. and Jones, T.A., *Important Bird
Areas in Europe*, ICBP/IWRB, Cambridge, 1989

Hale, W.G., *Waders*, Collins, London., 1980

Hayman, P.J., Marchant, J. and Prater, A.J.,
*Shorebirds: An Identification Guide to the
Waders of the World*, Croom Helm,
Beckenham, 1986

Hollom, P.A.D., Porter, R.F., Christensen, S. and
Willis, I., *Birds of the Middle East and North
Africa*, T. & A.D. Poyser, Calton, 1988

Jackson, C.E., *British Names of Birds*, Witherby,
London, 1968

Jonsson, L., *Birds of Europe*, Helm, London,
1992

Macleod, R.D., *Key to the Names of British
Birds*, Pitman, London, 1954

Meinertzhagen, R., 'The Speed and Altitude of
Bird Flight', *Ibis* 97 (1955) 81

Monroe, B.L., Jr., 'The New DNA–DNA Avian
Classification', *Britsh Birds* 85 (1992) 2

Nethersole-Thompson, D., *The Dotterel*, Collins,
London, 1973

Nethersole-Thompson, D. and M., *Greenshanks*,
Poyser, Calton, 1979

Nethersole-Thompson, D. and M., *Waders: Their
Breeding, Haunts and Watchers*, Poyser,
Calton, 1986

Oakes, C., '"Plover's Page" behaviour of Dunlin',
British Birds 41 (1948) 266

Ogilvie, M.A., *The Winter Birds*, Michael Joseph,
London, 1976

Page, G. and Whitacre, D.F., 'Raptor
Predation on wintering shorebirds', *Condor*
77 (1975) 73

Parr, R.G., 'Sequential polyandry by Golden
Plovers', *British Birds* 85 (1992) 309

Paz, U., *The Birds of Israel*, Christopher Helm,
Bromley, 1987

Pennington, M.G., 'Ringed Plovers nesting in
covered sites', *British Birds* 85 (1992) 498

Pienkowski, M.E. *Feeding Activities of wading
birds and shelducks at Teesmouth and some
further effects of loss of habitat*, Institute of
Terrestrial Ecology, Huntingdon, 1973

Raine, P., *Mediterranean Wildlife: The Rough
Guide*, Harrap Columbus, Bromley, 1990

Rhijn, J. van, *The Ruff: Individuality in a
Gregarious Wading Bird*, Poyser, London,
1991

Sibley, C.G. and Monroe, B.L., Jr., *Distribution
and Taxonomy of Birds of the World*, Yale
University Press, New Haven, 1990

Smith, P.C., and Evans, P.R., 'Studies of
shorebirds at Lindisfarne, Northumberland',
Wildfowl 24 (1973) 135

SCIENTIFIC NAMES

This list of waders found in the Western Palearctic is based on the order devised by Sibley and Monroe and follows the *British Birds* list of English names.

ROSTRATULIDAE
Painted Snipe *Rostratula benghalensis*
HAEMATOPODIDAE
Oystercatcher *Haematopus ostralegus*
RECURVIROSTRIDAE
Black-winged Stilt *Himantopus himantopus*
Avocet *Recurvirostra avosetta*
DROMADIDAE
Crab Plover *Dromas ardeola*
BURHINIDAE
Stone Curlew *Burhinus oedicnemus*
Senegal Thick-knee *Burhinus senegalensis*
GLAREOLIDAE
Cream-coloured Courser *Cursorius cursor*
Collared Pratincole *Glareola pratincola*
Black-winged Pratincole *Glareola nordmanni*
CHARADRIIDAE
Little Ringed Plover *Charadrius dubius*
Ringed Plover *Charadrius hiaticula*
Kittlitz's Plover *Charadrius pecuarius*
Kentish Plover *Charadrius alexandrinus*
Greater Sandplover *Charadrius leschenaultii*
Caspian Plover *Charadrius asiaticus*
Dotterel *Charadrius morinellus*
Golden Plover *Pluvialis apricaria*

Grey Plover *Pluvialis squatarola*
Spur-winged Plover *Hoplopterus spinosus*
Sociable Plover *Chettusia gregaria*
White-tailed Plover *Chettusia leucura*
Lapwing *Vanellus vanellus*
SCOLOPACIDAE
Knot *Calidris canutus*
Sanderling *Calidris alba*
Little Stint *Calidris minuta*
Temminck's Stint *Calidris temminckii*
Curlew Sandpiper *Calidris ferruginea*
Purple Sandpiper *Calidris maritiman*
Dunlin *Calidris alpina*
Broad-billed Sandpiper *Limicola falcinellus*
Ruff *Philomachus pugnax*
Jack Snipe *Lymnocryptes minimus*
Snipe *Gallinago gallinago*
Great Snipe *Gallinago media*
Woodcock *Scolopax rusticola*
Black-tailed Godwit *Limosa limosa*
Bar-tailed Godwit *Limosa lapponica*
Whimbrel *Numenius phaeopus*
Slender-billed Curlew *Numenius tenuirostris*
Curlew *Numenius arquata*
Spotted Redshank *Tringa erythropus*
Redshank *Tringa totanus*
Marsh Sandpiper *Tringa stagnatilis*
Greenshank *Tringa nebularia*
Green Sandpiper *Tringa ochropus*

INDEX

References in *italics* are to illustrations

Avocet
adaptations for feeding 51
camouflage 89
courtship display 102–5
feeding methods 41–2, 42, 50
flocking 62
life-span 126
mating ceremony 105, 105
pair-bond 113
preening 84
scratching 87
sleep 89
territorial defence 99

Blackcap 13

Courser, Cream-coloured 8, 165
adaptations for feeding 51, 53
breeding season 14
feeding methods 41
moult 73–4
reaction to danger 123
coursers 7
Curlew
adaptations for feeding 47, 51
age of first breeding 125
breeding season 90
courtship display 100, 101
diet 33

distraction display 122–3, 146–7
eggs 115
feeding methods 40, 48–9
finding food 55, 57
flocking 65, 66, 67
incubation 117
migration 23
mortality rate
plumage 66, 74, 75
roosting 68, 69
sexual dimorphism 91
territorial display 98–9
time of feeding 69
young 119
curlews 7
adaptations for feeding 50
migration 23
Curlew, Slender-billed
migration 18, 18–19
Curlew, Stone 7, 9, 10
adaptations for feeding 50, 51
age of first breeding 125
breeding season 90
clutch-size 116
eggs 118
feeding methods 40
migration 22
second clutches 116
time of feeding 58–9

Dotterel
breeding season 100
feeding methods 36

incubation 117
migration 20–21, 26, 139
moult 82
sexual dimorphism 91
time of feeding 59
young 120
Dunlin 27
age of first breeding 125
aggression 95
breeding season 100
body weight 24
diet 24
distraction display 122–3
feeding methods 37, 43
finding food 55, 146–7
flocking 63, 65, 66
migration 14, 19, 21, 24, 25–6
moult 78–80
plumage 82
roosting 68
site fidelity 100
time of feeding 58, 69
young 119

Godwit, Bar-tailed 44
breeding season 91
diet 34
feeding methods 48–9, 49–50
finding food 55, 56, 146–7
flocking 66
migration 14, 19
roosting 68

site fidelity 91–2
time of feeding 69
Godwit, Black-tailed
  body-weight 24, *44*
  brood-patch 82
  feeding methods *48–9,*
  49–50
  migration 17–18,
  18–19, 24
  roosting 68
godwits 7
  age of first breeding
  125
  migration 23
  roosting 69
Greenshank *111*
  breeding season 100
  courtship display 100,
  101
  diet 34
  feeding methods 43
  finding food *161*
  plumage 66, 82
Gull, Black-headed 36,
  70–72, *70–71*

Harrier, Marsh 114,
  120

Kestrel 66, 120
Knot
  camouflage 121–2
  courtship display 100
  diet 33
  distraction display
  122–3
  flocking 64, *65,* 67
  migration 24
  roosting 68, 69
  time of feeding 69

Lapwing 7, 8, 10
  breeding territory 92
  diet 34
  feeding methods 36

flocking 70–72, *70–71*
injury-feigning display
  122
life-span 126
migration 14, *15,* 23,
  25, 28
roosting 69
site-fidelity, lack of 92
sleep 88, *88*
territorial display 92,
  93
young 120

Merlin 62, 64
Moorhen 124

Owl, Short-eared 64
Oystercatcher 7, 9
  adaptations for feeding
  52–5, *54*
  age of first breeding
  125
  aggression 61, *60,* 66,
  124–5, *124*
  diet 33, 34
  feeding methods *38–9,*
  40
  finding food 56–7
  flocking 64, *65,* 66, 67
  life-span 126
  migration 14, 19
  mortality 125–6
  moult 76–8
  nest camouflage 114
  pair-bond 99–100, 112
  plumage *77*
  roosting 68, 69
  scratching 69
  territorial display 96–7,
  97
  time of feeding 69
  young 119

Pelican, White 64
Peregrine 124

Phalarope, Grey
  feeding methods 43,
  162–3
  sleep 88
Phalarope, Red-necked *8*
  adaptations for feeding
  53, 55
  breeding season 100
  brood-patch 82
  eggs and egg-laying 114
  feeding methods 43, *44*
  incubation 117
  plumage 75
  sleep 88
  young 119
phalaropes 10
  incubation 117
  moult 82
  sexual dimorphism 91
  young 119, 120
Pigeon, Wood 114
Plover, Caspian 10
  migration 17
Plover, Crab 7, 9
  clutch-size 116
  eggs 114
Plover, Egyptian
  incubation 117
Plover, Golden *27*
  diet 34
  feeding methods 36
  flocking *70–71*
  migration 23, 25, *25,*
  26
  pair-bond 113
  polyandry 113
  roosting 69, 70–72
  site fidelity 92
  territorial display 98
  young 119
Plover, Grey
  feeding methods 36–7,
  36–7
  feeding territory 60–61
  finding food 55–66, *59*

flocking 67
migration 19
roosting 68, 69
young 119
Plover, Kentish
nest-scrape 113
Plover, Kittlitz's 11, 28,
166
Plover, Little Ringed
injury-feigning display
122
migration 13
nest-scrape 113
Plover, Ringed 8
aggression 94–5, 94–5
breeding territory 93
camouflage 120–121,
122
double-brooding 116
eggs 115
flocking 66, 68
migration 18–20, 20, 22
moult 76
nest camouflage 114
nest-scrape 113
plumage 76, 82
roosting 68, 69
second clutches 116
territorial display 93–5
time of feeding 69
young 119
plovers 7
adaptations for feeding
50, 51
breeding territory 92
feeding methods 36
flocking 70–72
injury-feigning display
122
Plover, Sociable
migration 26, 168
flocking 70
Plover, Spur-winged 159
aggression 125
breeding territory 92

feeding flocks 11
incubation 117
migration 11
second clutches 116
territorial display 92
Pratincole, Black-winged
10
migration 22
Pratincole, Collared 10
clutch-size 116
feeding methods 40–41,
41
flocking 62
migration 22
moult 76
roosting 69–70
time of feeding 58
pratincoles 7

Redshank 9
aggression 96
breeding territory 96
chick-carrying 123
courtship display
100–102, 112
eggs 115
feeding methods 37–8
finding food 57, 146–7
migration 14, 24, 25
mortality rage 125
nest-scrape 113–14
pair-bond 112
plumage 82
reaction to danger 124
roosting 66, 69
second clutches 116
time of feeding 58, 69
young 119
Redshank, Spotted
feeding methods 43,
135
finding food 161
flocking 64
migration 14, 17, 24–5
moult 80–82

Redwing 114
Rook 36
Ruff
brood-patch 82
courtship display 99,
106–9, 107
distraction display 123
feeding methods 40, 43
incubation 117
migration 14
moult 80, 81
plumage 73, 80
polygyny 106–9
sexual dimorphism 91

Sanderling
adaptations for feeding
55
body-weight 24
breeding season 91
double-brooding 116
finding food 55, 146–7,
155
incubation 117
migration 11, 12,
13–14, 24
moult 79
roosting 68
time of feeding 69
Sandpiper, Broad-billed
migration 17
young 119
Sandpiper, Common
body-weight 24
breeding season 90
chick-carrying 123
courtship display 112
diet 24
feeding methods 40
flocking 62
migration 24, 26, 62
stretching 86
Sandpiper, Curlew
moult 78
young 120

Sandpiper, Green
 migration 21–2
 moult 80
 plumage 66
 re-use of nests 114, *115*
Sandpiper, Marsh
 migration 17
Sandpiper, Purple
 diet 33
 distraction display
 122–3
 feeding methods *38–9,*
 50
 finding food 56, *131*
 moult 78
sandpipers 7–10
 age of first breeding
 125
 aggression 66, 95
 breeding territory 95
 flocking 64, 66
 migration 23
 nesting material 114
 nest-scrapes 113
 plumage 73
Sandpiper, Terek
 feeding methods 40,
 144
Sandpiper, Wood
 nests 114
Shelduck *94–5*
Snipe
 courtship display 102
 eggs 115
 feeding methods 43–4,
 48
 plumage 75

reaction to danger 124
territorial display 97–8,
 98
 young 119
Snipe, Great
 camouflage 121
 courtship display *109,*
 110
 feeding methods 46
Snipe, Jack
 feeding methods 44–6
Snipe, Painted 7, *8,* 11,
 28
 courtship display 106,
 167
 polyandry 106
 roosting 69–70
 sexual dimorphism 91
snipes
 adaptations for feeding
 46, 50
Stilt, Black-winged 7, *9*
 courtship display
 105–6
 distraction display 123
 feeding methods 42
 flocking 62
 nesting colonially with
 other species 114
 nesting material 114
 scratching *85,* 87
Stint, Little *8*
Stint, Temminck's *133*
 age of first breeding
 125
 double-brooding 116
 incubation 117

mortality rate 125
 pair-bond 110–11
 polyandry 111
 polygyny 111

Thick-knee, Senegal 7
 adaptations for feeding
 50
Turnstone
 adaptations for feeding
 51–2, *53*
 age of first breeding
 125
 diet 33
 feeding methods 38–40,
 38–9
 flocking 68
 scratching 87
 site-fidelity 91

Whimbrel
 adaptations for feeding
 51
 migration 19
Woodcock 9
 adaptations for feeding
 50–51, *52*
 camouflage 121
 chick-carrying 123, *123*
 courtship display 102,
 103
 diet *140*
 eggs 115–16
 feeding methods 40,
 46–8
 reaction to danger 124
 second clutches 116

HAMLYN

NATURAL HISTORY BOOKS

A complete range of Hamlyn Natural History titles is available from all good bookshops or by mail order direct from the publisher. Payment can be made by credit card or cheque/postal order in the following ways:

BY PHONE
Phone through your order on our special *Credit Card Hotline* on **0933 410 511**. Speak to our customer service team during office hours (9 a.m. to 5 p.m.) or leave a message on the answer machine, quoting your full credit card number plus expiry date and your full name and address. Please also quote the reference number NATHIS 3.

BY POST
Simply fill out the order form below (photocopies are acceptable) and send it with your payment to:
Cash Sales Department,
Reed Book Services Ltd.,
P.O. Box 5,
Rushden,
Northants, NN10 6YX

NATHIS 3

I wish to order the following titles:

Title	ISBN	Price	Quantity	Total
Hamlyn Guide to the Birds of Britain and Europe	0 600 57492 X	£8.99	....	£ ....
Photographic Guide to Birds of Britain and Europe	0 600 57861 5	£9.99	....	£ ....
Where to Watch Birds in Britain and Europe	0 600 58007 5	£9.99	....	£ ....
Behaviour Guide: Birds of Prey	0 540 01277 7	£14.99	....	£ ....
Behaviour Guide: Seabirds	0 600 57951 4	£14.99	....	£ ....

Add £2.00 for postage and packing if your order is worth £10.00 or less £ ....

Grand Total £ ....

Name _____ (block capitals)

Address _____

_____ Postcode _____

I enclose a cheque/postal order for £ _____ made payable to Reed Book Services Ltd
or
Please debit my ☐ Access   ☐ Visa   ☐ American Express   ☐ Diners

account number ☐☐☐☐ ☐☐☐☐ ☐☐☐☐ ☐☐☐☐

by £ _____ Expiry date _____ Signature _____

SPECIAL OFFER: FREE POSTAGE AND PACKAGING FOR ALL ORDERS OVER £10.00, add £2.00 for p+p if your order is £10.00 or less.

Whilst every effort is made to keep our prices low, the publisher reserves the right to increase the prices at short notice.
Your order will be dispatched within 5 days, but please allow up to 28 days for delivery, subject to availability.
Registered office: Michelin House, 81 Fulham Road, London SW3 6RB.
Registered in England no 1974080.

If you do not wish your name to be used by other carefully selected organizations for promotional purposes, please tick this box ☐